Veikko Jääskeläinen

Linear Programming and Budgeting

PETROCELLI/CHARTER   NEW YORK

Studentlitteratur · Sweden

ISBN/Petrocelli 0-88405-433-0
First published in the United States
in 1976 by Petrocelli/Charter,
          division of Mason/Charter Publishers, Inc.,
          641 Lexington Ave.
          New York, N.Y. 10022

Second printing
Printed in Sweden
Studentlitteratur
Lund 1976
ISBN/Studentlitteratur 91-44-40611-8

Preface

The present English edition of Linear Programming and Budgeting brings to a wider audience the original Finnish text which was first published in 1972.

Some form of budgeting is today an absolutely necessary tool for the financial planning of business firms. Even banks and various public institutions which channel funds, guarantees and other types of financial assistance to business firms regard a well functioning budgetary system a necessary precondition for their positive decisions. When auditors evaluate the performance of the management they use the status of the firm´s budgetary system as one criterion.

Quantitative methods and decision support systems are presently being utilized to help the management in generating alternative budgets based on varying sets of assumptions and answering "what if...." questions. This does not, of course, imply that the important decisions about the firm´s future action alternatives were to be automated. The final decisions on future budgets are made by top management in co-operation with the controller and the heads of product divisions. All assumptions and other essential aspects of future plans must be thoroughly reviewed and weighed against each other in the process. However, this process can be made more effective through a dialogue between the participants in the budgetary process and the decision support systems. The participants can then receive fast answers to their questions about the economic consequences of alternative action programs.

The technique of linear programming makes it possible to optimize the firm´s profit objective under constraints on sales, production capacity, purchases, financing, utilization of personnel and physical facilities, etc. In addition to the optimal program under a specific set of constraints the solution to a linear programming problem provides us with a set of dual evaluators or shadow prices of the limited resources. The shadow prices draw the attention of management to the points where the removal of bottlenecks will bring about the largest increase in the profit objective.

Professor Jääskeläinen´s text requires that the reader has some familiarity with the basic notions of financial and cost accounting as well as budgeting concepts. On the other hand, no extensive knowledge of quantitative methods is a prerequisite since it is assumed that the linear programming problems presented in the text are solved by utilizing commercially available computer codes provided by practically all computer manufacturers.

The pedagogic layout of the text is masterly. The reader is carefully guided by small steps through a series of examples beginning with very simple and easily understood breakeven models and ending with more complicated, and also more realistic multi-period multi-plant models.

The closing chapters of the text give the reader an overview of the budgetary control process and an analysis of conflicting goals as well as an introduction to strategic planning models.

Both the student and the practitioner can greatly profit by reading this text.

Sandor Asztély
University of Gothenburg
Göteborg - Sweden

Introduction

Firms are presently moving into the use of linear programming models as a basis of the budgeting process. The first optimization models employed by pioneering firms were often called "plant models." This name refers to a mathematical model representing a technical production process. It is natural that such names were used considering the educational and occupational background of the developers of the early models. The early developers were often employed in production management or in associated staff positions. Recently it has become evident that optimization models must be closely tied together with the budget models of the firm. This implies that model builders must be thoroughly familiar with the concepts and techniques used in budgeting.

The most likely candidates of model builders familiar with budgets are accountants. However, their educational background has traditionally included little that helps to understand the concepts and techniques of model buildning. The purpose of this text is to help accountants with traditional backgrounds to understand the basic concepts of budget models and the techniques for building them.

Model building is team work and the teams will also include operations researchers, mathematicians, as well as marketing and production personnel. Hopefully the text will also provide these persons with diverse backgrounds with a better understanding of the budgeting process.

The text is based on a series of numerical examples, i.e., no attempt is made to present a general theory of either linear programming or budgeting. The idea is that by providing a series of progressively more complicated examples the text will give the reader with no background in linear programming an intuitive grasp of the fundamentals of this technique and prepare him for more abstract and more general presentations of the underlying theory. The introductory chapter includes an example that gives the reader a feeling about the solution of a linear programming problem. The three following chapters present a series of examples beginning with a single-plant and single-period model and ending with two-plant two-period models that include the basic elements of a multi-plant and multi-period model needed to represent the planning situation of a modern large firm.

Chapter 5 contains a series of examples introducing to the reader the possibility of using optimization models in the control phase of operations. The remaining chapters treat the uses of optimization models in the area of strategic planning. Strategic planning is an area with relatively few reported applications of optimization techniques but with a great future potential. It may well be that the largest benefits to the top management from the use of optimization models will accumulate in the future from the application of these models into strategic planning problems.

No prior knowledge of linear programming is expected of the reader. It is assumed that the exercises at the end of each chapter are solved with commercially available computer codes. This implies that the required familiarity with data processing techniques is also minimal. It is assumed that the reader is familiar with the most common concepts of Management Accounting.

Veikko Jääskeläinen

Contents

1 Generalization of Breakeven Analysis with Linear Programming

Traditional Analysis of a Single Product

The purpose of the present chapter is to introduce to the reader the use of linear programming in the planning of the operations of the firm. We begin with the traditional breakeven analysis and demonstrate how linear programming can be used to generalize this analysis to include many products which are produced and sold subject to various diverse constraints.

Figure 1 presents the traditional breakeven analysis of a single product. The vertical axis shows the revenue and costs in monetary units. The horizontal axis indicates the volume of operations during the period under consideration. The volume of operations may be measured in sales dollars, units of product manufactured and sold, or the quantity of output expressed as a percentage of total production capacity.

The horizontal line represents the fixed costs which are assumed to remain constant over the possible range of output. The sloping line that originates at the intersection of the vertical axis and the horizontal fixed cost line represents the total costs which are the sum of fixed and variable costs. It is assumed, in other words, that the costs can be classified in two categories and that the variable costs are directly proportional to the volume of production.

The 45 degree sloping line originating at the intersection of the axes is the revenue line. The assumption behind this line is that the selling price of the product remains fixed over the possible range of output. The difference between the selling price and variable costs is the contribution margin of the product. The contribution per unit of product multiplied by the number of units sold gives the total contribution to fixed costs and profit.

The breakeven point shows the volume of operations at which the total revenue and the total cost break even. At this volume he firm neither makes nor loses money. If the management knows that the firm is operating at a volume to the right of the breakeven point, it also knows

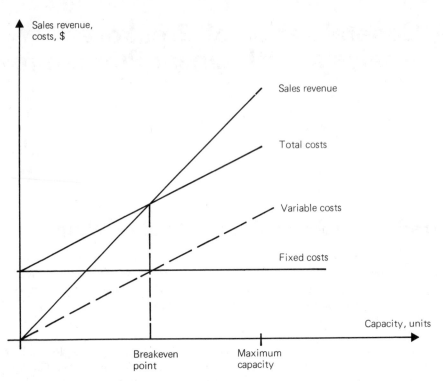

Figure 1. Traditional breakeven analysis.

that the operations are profitable, if the actual revenue and costs equal
the planned revenue and costs. On the other hand, if the firm is operating
at a volume to he left of the breakeven point, the management knows
withhout further analysis that the firm is losing money. The traditional
breakeven analysis is designed to stress the psychological qualitative
difference between profit and loss. For most managers, the difference
between $ 500 profit and $ 500 loss is not the same as the difference
between $ 5 500 profit and $ 4 500 profit, or the difference between
$ 4 500 loss and $ 5 500 loss, although on the same continuous scale all
these differences are equal.

However, the breakeven point is not the only point of interest in
Figure 1. The figure also shows the point that gives the maximum profit
to the firm. Profit is maximized when the volume of operations is as
high as possible. The difference between the revenue line and the total
cost line reaches its maximum at this point.

Deducting the fixed costs from the total costs gives the variable costs.
The broken line from the origin in Figure 1 represents the variable
costs. If we compare the revenue line and the variable cost line, we
notice that the difference between the revenue and the variable costs is
maximized at the same point at which the profit is at the maximum. In

2

other words, to maximize profit the firm must maximize its total contribution.

We next analyze the profit and contribution relationships with the help of algebraic concepts. This brings us closer to the concepts employed in a linear programming problem. Let

b = maximum volume of operations, hours,
a = required production capacity, hours per unit of product,
p = selling price, \$ per unit of product,
c = variable costs, \$ per unit of product,
F = fixed costs, \$.

Using these concepts we can formulate the remaining concepts employed in the breakeven analysis:

$$px = \text{total revenue, \$}$$
$$cx = \text{total variable costs, \$}$$
$$cx + F = \text{total costs, \$}$$
$$(p-c)x - F = \text{profit for the period, \$}$$
$$ax = \text{capacity used in production, hours.}$$

We know that profit is maximized whenever the total contribution is at its maximum. The contribution is the difference between the revenue and the variable costs:

$$Z = px - cx = (p-c)x.$$

We also know that he total contribution cannot be made arbitrarily large because the production cannot exceed the available capacity. The capacity used in the production must be less than or equal to the maximum available capacity:

$$ax \leq b.$$

We can now present the problem of the maximization of the total contribution in the form of a linear programming problem:

Maximize $Z = (p-c)x$
subject to
$$ax \leq b,$$
$$x \geq 0.$$

The inequality $x \geq 0$ prevents us from considering negative amounts of products. In traditional breakeven analysis this condition is observed implicitly. However, the condition must be explicitly stated if we wish

3

to write out a formal linear programming problem.

The problem at hand is so simple that the solution can be found without any formal methods. Optimum production, x', and maximum contribution, Z', are given by

$$x' = \frac{b}{a}, \qquad Z' = (p-c)\frac{b}{a}.$$

The maximum profit is the difference between the maximum contribution and fixed costs:

$$Z' - F = (p-c)\frac{b}{a} - F.$$

Every analysis of the planning problems of the firm is carried out by making a number of assumptions about the conditions under which the firm will operate. It is important to know the best possible course of action under this set of assumptions. However, it is at least as important to know what happens to the best alternative if the conditions themselves can be changed. The firm under analysis is maximizing the total contribution subject to a given amount of production capacity. After the solution is found it is important to know how much the contribution would increase if an additional unit of production capacity were made available. When the management knows the per unit increase in contribution it can evaluate the possibilities of obtaining an additional unit of capacity. A possibility might be to work overtime. Another possibility is the introduction of the second shift. A third possibility is the purchase of capacity hours from some othe firm. If the cost of an additional unit of capacity is less than the increase in contribution the management must, of course, modify the original optimal program and produce more units than is indicated by the optimal value of variable x'.

Let us consider a new program where the available production capacity is b+1 hours and all other things remain unchanged. We can write this new problem in the linear programming form as follows:

Maximize $Z = (p-c)x$
subject to
$$ax \leq b+1$$
$$x \geq 0.$$

The new optimal program x'' and the maximum contribution Z'' are given by

$$x'' = \frac{b+1}{a}$$

and

$$Z'' = (p-c)\frac{b+1}{a} \ .$$

The change in the total contribution resulting from the one hour change in the production capacity is given by

$$Z'' - Z' = (p-c)\frac{b+1}{a} - (p-c)\frac{b}{a} = \frac{p-c}{a} \ .$$

The solution method of linear programming generates the respective quantities simultaneously with the solution of the original problem. These quantities are called shadow prices associated with the restrictions of the original problem.

Example: Let us consider the following numerical example and apply the concepts developed above:

1 000 = maximum volume of operations, hours,
    2 = required production capacity, hours per unit,
  10 = selling price, $/unit,
    5 = variable costs, $/unit,
2 000 = fixed costs, $.

Substitution of these figures into our general problem gives

Maximize $Z = (10-5)x$
subject to
$$2x \leq 1\ 000$$
$$x \geq 0.$$

The optimal solution of the problem is

$$x' = \frac{1\ 000}{2} = 500 \text{ units,}$$

$$Z' = (10-5)500 = \$\ 2\ 500.$$

The net profit before tax for the period is $\$\ 2\ 500 - \$\ 2\ 000 = \$\ 500$. The breakeven point in units of product is by definition

$$Z - F = 0, \text{ or } (10-5)x - 2\ 000 = 0$$

which gives

$$x = 400 \text{ units.}$$

The increase in the total contribution resulting from a one unit increase in production capacity is

$$\frac{(10-5)}{2} = \$ \ 2.5 \text{ per hour.}$$

If the firm can get an additional production hour for less than $ 2.5/hour it would pay to change the optimal program and acquire the additional hours.

Multi-Product Breakeven Analysis

Breakeven analysis can be extended to multi-product firms. Usually the products of a multi-product firm are not equally profitable. It is normally possible to single out without any penetrating analysis some products that are outstanding and other products which are clearly unprofitable. This approach may lead to the idea of ranking the products in the order of profitability and improving the profit by eliminating the most unprofitable prducts.

If this idea is carried to the extreme, we should eliminate all but the best product and concentrate all our efforts on it. The best product can be found by computing the contribution per unit and choosing the product with the highest per unit contribution.

Multi-product breakeven analysis attempts to eliminate the errors inherent in this extreme attitude. First of all, the firm may not be able to sell more than a limited amount of the product that gives the highest contribution. Secondly, the contribution per unit of product may not be the relevant parameter to consider, if the production capacity is limited. The product with the highest per unit contribution may not be the best if we compute the contribution per bottleneck factor which is the production capacity. Some other product with a lower per unit contribution may require less production capacity and may be ranked higher if we consider the contribution per capacity hour.

We must therefore observe that both the selling possibilities and the producition capacity may limit the operations. Let us consider the following example:

Product	Contribution $/unit	Req.Capacity hours/unit	Contribution $/hour	Demand units	Production Volume
A	2.-	2	1.-	250	x_1
B	3.-	4	0.75	200	x_2
C	5.-	10	0.50	70	x_3

The firm produces and sells three products, A, B, and C. Product C is the best if we consider the contribution per unit of product. When we observe the demand for products and the available production capacity, 1 800 hours, it is evident that no single product can absorb all capacity. On the other hand, we cannot sell all products to the upper limit of existing demand:

$$(2)250 + (4)200 + (10)70 > 1\ 800.$$

The capacity required by all products is greater than the total available capacity. It follows that we must rank the products by contribution per production hour and the rank of product C is the lowest. The breakeven chart based on these figures has been presented in Figure 2.

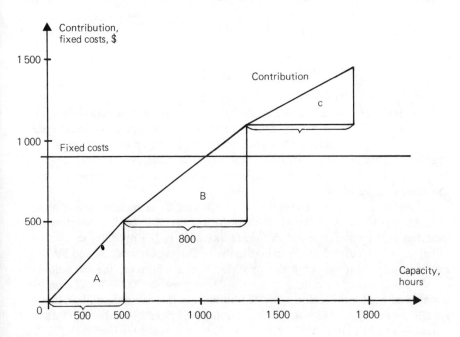

Figure 2. Multiproduct breakeven analysis.

The contribution generated by the products is presented in Figure 2 beginning with product A which gives the highest per unit contribution. The required capacity is shown on the horizontal axis and the total contribution on the vertical axis. A full utilization of the sales possibilites of product A requires 500 hours of capacity and generates $ 500 contribution. The corresponding figures for product B are 800 hours and $ 600. Finally, product C requires 700 hours and generates $ 350 contribution.

The total available capacity is 1 800 hours. This implies that the maximum contribution is generated by the program which produces 250 units of product A, 200 units of product B, and 50 units of product C. An additional unit of production capacity would increase the contribution by $ 0.50 which is the contribution per hour of product C. The breakeven point is given by the intersection of the fixed cost line and the kinked total contribution line.

The problem can also be written in a linear programming form:

$$\text{Maximize } Z = 2x_1 + 3x_2 + 5x_3$$

subject to

$$
\begin{aligned}
x_1 & & & \leq 250 \\
& x_2 & & \leq 200 \\
& & x_3 & \leq 70
\end{aligned}
\Bigg\} \text{ Sales}
$$

$$2x_1 + 4x_2 + 10x_3 \leq 1\ 800 \qquad \text{Production}$$

and

$$x_1 \geq 0,\ x_2 \geq 0,\ x_3 \geq 0.$$

This problem can be solved by inspection because it is clearly a special case. Each of the upper limits of sales possibilities include just one variable. This leaves a single constraint that ties the variables together. This is the constraint which requires that the capacity used in the production of the various products must be less than or equal to the total available capacity, 1 800 hours.

In this special case we can find the optimum by computing for each variable x_i the ratio of the coefficient of the variable in the objective function to the coefficient of the same variable in the production constraint, by selecting the variables with the highest ratios and by setting their values as high as possible. In our example, the variable x_i which represents product A has the highest ratio, $2/2 = 1$. The sales constraint limits the value of x_1 to 250 units. The variable x_2 has the next highest ratio, $3/4 = 0.75$, and the highest possible value for this variable is 200 units. Finally, the production constraint limits the value of the remaining variable x_3 to 50 units:

$$10x_3 = 1\ 800 - 2(250) - 4(200)$$

or

$$x_3 = 50.$$

This is, of course, precisely the same analysis that was carried out in order to set up Figure 2. It is the purpose of the remaining sections of this chapter to demonstrate that linear programming allows us to consider problems which are more general than the present exemple. In other woerds, we generalize the analysis to problems where there are several constraints which tie the different products together. We can then no longer use the two-dimensional breakeven chart to analyze these problems but with algebraic methods we can find solutions to them as easily as to a problem involving only two dimensions.

Optimal Product Mix and Linear Programming

Data Collection

When linear programming models for solving complicated management problems are being formulated, it is normally impossible to know in advance which constraints will bind the optimal solution. It follows that we must attempt to list all potential constraining factors and collect data for the formulation of these restrictions. After the solution we may find that some of these constraints do not effectively bind the solution. Then we know that we could have disregarded the constraints to begin with - but this is only after the model has been built.

Data collection for the formulation of the model can be a very substantial and time consuming task. We must pass by this stage in a textbook and assume that the necessary data has already been collected. A beginning student reading a textbook may therefore not appreciate the difficulties involved in data collection.

With these reservations in mind we will formulate a small model of a firm which produces and sells two products, A and B. At the end of the preceding section a reference was made to the case with which algebraic solutions can be formed for multiproduct problems. The reason for assuming now that the product mix consists of two products only is that we wish to compare the algebraic solution presented in the appendix to a graphic solution to be derived in this chapter.

The sales price of product A is $ 900 per unit and that of product B $ 800 per unit. Demand forecasts have beend developed for both products assuming that the sales of the products do not interact. The maximum amount of product A that could be sold is 6 units. The respective upper limit for product B is 10 units. Product A is sold with one period credit, i.e., the cash collections of the sales revenue of the planning period are received only after the horizon. On the other hand, one half of the sales revenue of product B is received during the same period in which the sales are realized, the rest maturing one period after. In the present exemple we assume that there are no variable selling costs.

Production management estimates on the basis of standard cost data that the capacity required for manufacturing one unit of product A is 10 hours whereas a unit of product B requires 20 hours. The total available capacity for the period is 160 hours. The variable manufacturing costs of product A are $ 300 per unit and they are all paid in cash at the same rate at which the production proceeds. The variable manufacturing costs of product B are $ 600 per unit. These costs are also paid in cash.

The financial department has developed a balance sheet for the beginning of the planning period as well as a budget for fixed overhead costs. The beginning balance sheet is the following:

Beginning Balance Sheet

Assets			Liabilities		
Current Assets			Current Liabilities		
Cash	1 000		Accounts Payable	900	
Accounts			Short-term Debt	10 000	10 900
Receivable	6 800				
Inventories	6 000	13 800	Equity		7 400
Fixed Assets		4 500			
		$ 18 300			$ 18 300

We are developing a short-run plan. This implies that the fixed overhead costs are incurred regardless of the production and sales budget. We assume that the following fixed overhead budget has been prepared for the planning period:

Fixed Overhead Budget

Depreciation	$ 500.-
Expenses payable in cash	1 900.-
Accruals	800.-
Total	$ 3 200.-

We assume, in other words, that fixed expenses can be classified in three categories. Depreciation does not involve any cash movement. Other expenses are either payable in cash during the planning period or cause a cash payment in later periods.

These data are used to formulate a restriction which requires that the funds tied in the planned operations will not exceed the available funds. The initial cash balance as well as the cash collections of accounts receivable are available for the financing of operations. On the other hand, we must reserve funds for the payment of the accounts payable balance of $ 900. The repayments of existing loans require $ 2 100 and the fixed costs involve a cash payment of $ 1 900. In addition, we plan to maintain a minimum cash balance of $ 500. This minimum balance is considered necessary for meeting unexpected needs of cash which may result due to the uncertainty about the future events.

Formulation of the Model

We begin the formulation of the model by setting up the objective which we attempt to achieve. The objective is to maximize the profit which in the short run is the same as the maximization of the contribution. We must therefore formulate the expression for the total contribution. The contribution per unit of product is the difference between the sales price and the variable costs:

	Product	
	A	B
Sales price, $/unit	900.-	800.-
Variable costs, »	300.-	600.-
Contribution margin, $/unit	600.-	200.-

The production and sales of product A is represented by the variable x_1. Similarly, the production and sales of product B is represented by the variable x_2. The contribution margin per unit of product multiplied by the number of units gives the contribution of each product. The total

11

contribution, Z, is the sum of the product contributions:

$$(1 - 1) \qquad Z = 600x_1 + 200x_2.$$

Marketing management estimates that we can sell neither product in unlimited quantities. The production of a product must not exceed its estimated demand because in the present example we do not yet consider the possibility of producing for stock. The estimated upper limit of the demand of each product is the following:

$$(1 - 2) \qquad x_1 \leq 6,$$
$$x_2 \leq 10.$$

The planned use of production capacity must not exceed the available capacity. The production of one unit of product A requires 10 hours of production capacity. The number of units produced is given by x_1. Therefore, the total amount of production capacity required for the making of product A is $10x_1$. Similarly, the capacity required for the making of product B is $20x_2$. We get the restriction

$$(1 - 3) \qquad 10x_1 + 20x_2 \leq 160.$$

The cash constraint which relates the funds required to the funds available is developed in two stages. In the first stage we observe the cash receipts and disbursements that can be considered fixed regardless of the planned sales and production:

Funds Initially Available		
Beginning Cash Balance	$ 1 000	
Accounts Receivable	6 800	7 800
Fixed Cash Expenses		
Accounts Payable Balance	$ 900	
Repayment of Loans	2 100	
Fixed Expenses	1 900	4 900
Difference		2 900
Required Minimum Ending Cash Balance		500
Operations		$ 2 400

We note that after the beginning balance sheet items and the fixed cost budget have been observed, we have $ 2 400 available for the financing of the planned operations.

In the second stage we take into account the cash receipts and disbursements caused by the planned operations. The only source of cash receipts in the present example is the sale of the two products. The sales price of product A is $ 900 per unit. The total sales revenue is the price multiplied by the number of units sold, $900x_1$. Since we are selling with one period credit, zero percent of this revenue is collected during the period. Cash receipts from the sale of product A are $ $(0)900x_1 = \$ 0$. The sales price of product B is $ 800 per unit. One half of the sales revenue is collected during the same period. Cash collections for product B are therefore $ $(0.5)800x_2 = \$ 400x_2$.

The same way we compute the cash disbursements resulting from the variable costs of production. We assume that the variable costs of both products are paid in cash during the period they are incurred. Cash disbursements are, in other words, 100 percent of the variable costs:

$$(1)300x_1 + (1)600x_2 = 300x_1 + 600x_2 .$$

The constraint is formulated by requiring that the cash disbursements for planned operations must not exceed the cash available plus the cash collections resulting from operations:

$$300x_1 + 600x_2 \leqq 2\,400 + (0)900x_1 + (0.5)800x_2$$

This can be simplified to form an inequality

$$(1 - 4) \qquad 300x_1 + 200x_2 \leqq 2\,400 .$$

In every linear programming problem we must require that all variables are nonnegative:

$$(1 - 5) \qquad x_1 \geq 0 \text{ and } x_2 \geq 0 .$$

We have now developed a mathematical model of the planning situation. Our problem is to maximize the total contribution subject to the constraints (1 - 2) to (1 - 5). We cannot find the solution by the use of the approach presented in Figure 2 because we now have two constraints, the capacity constraint and the cash constraint, which tie the production quantities together. In other words, the variables x_1 and x_2 appear now in both inequality (1 - 3) and inequality (1 - 4).

Graphic Solution

We formulated on purpose such a simple problem which can be solved
with the help of a geometric figure. This enables us to compare the
graphic solution to a computer solution presented in the Appendix.
Let the horizontal axis represent the production and sales of product A,
x_1, and the vertical axis the production and sales of product B, x_2.
Figure 3 represents this situation. We first draw the solution space
bounded by the inequalities (1 - 2) to (1 - 5). Next we find a point in
this area that maximizes the objective function (1 - 1).

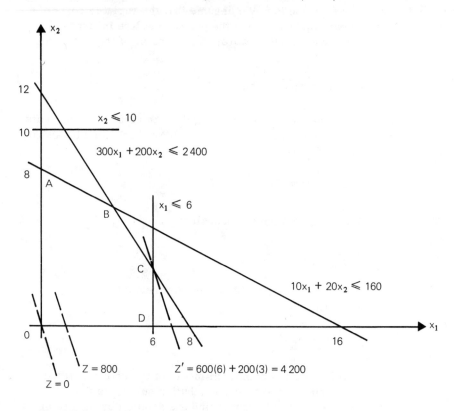

Figure 3. Graphic solution to the sample problem.

We begin by drawing the inequalities (1 - 2). The first inequality is
represented by a vertical line that cuts the x_1-axis at the point $x_1 = 6$.
The second inequality is again represented by a horizontal line that
cuts the x_2-axis at the point $x_2 = 10$. The solution must be found either
on the line $x_1 = 6$ or to the left of it. On the other hand, the solution

14

must lie either on the line $x_2 = 10$ or below it.

We next draw the constraint representing the production capacity. We disregard for the moment the inequality sign in (1 - 3) and consider it to be an equation representing a straight line. We can easily draw the line by finding two points through which the line passes. The most convenient points are the ones where the line cuts the axis. We first find the point on the x_2-axis by setting $x_1 = 0$ and solving for x_2:

$$x_1 = 0,$$

$$x_2 = \frac{160}{20} = 8.$$

The second point is found by setting $x_2 = 0$ and solving for x_1:

$$x_1 = \frac{160}{10} = 16,$$

$$x_2 = 0.$$

The line passing through these points is presented in Figure 3. The solution must be either on this line, or, observing now the inequality sign of (1 - 3), to the southwest of the line. If the constraint had been of the form $10x_1 + 20x_2 \geq 160$, the solution would have been either on the line or to the northeast of the line.

We finally draw the line representing the cash constraint (1 - 4) by finding the points where the line cuts the axes. These points are

$$x_1 = 0, \qquad \qquad x_1 = 8,$$
$$\text{and}$$
$$x_2 = 12, \qquad \qquad x_2 = 0.$$

Observing again the direction of the inequality sign we note that the solution must be either on the line or to the southwest of it.

The first nonnegativity constraint requires that the solution must be either on the x_1-axis or to the north of it. The second constraint limits the solution space to the x_2-axis or to the east of it. The solution space is therefore the area 0ABCD.

The objective function (1 - 1) resembles an equation for a straight line. If we give Z a specific value we in fact obtain an equation for a straight line. Let this value be arbitrarily specified to be zero:

$$Z = 0 = 600x_1 + 200x_2.$$

The resulting equation has been drawn in Figure 3 with a broken line which passes through the origin. We next select another arbitrary value for Z. Let us assume, for example, that Z = 800. The resulting equation $600x_1 + 200x_2 = 800$ has also been drawn in Figure 3 with a broken line. We can now see that the new line is parallel to the line Z = 0 and is to the northeast of the first line. The function $Z = 600x_1 + 200x_2$ can thus be represented with a set of parallel lines such that the value of the function is constant on a given line and increases when we move to a higher line.

An intuitive solution to our problem can now be found. We must find a line that is parallel to the broken lines and which is as far to the northeast as possible but still touches the solution space OABCD. It is evident that such a line can be drawn through point C.

The solution space of a general linear programming problem has many dimensions and we can no longer represent it with a twodimensional figure. The solution space is a convex polyhedral cone and the objective function is a hyperplane and in order to find the "highest" point where the plane touches the cone we must use algebra. However, we will not present in this text the formal solution method. We will assume instead that the remaining problems are solved using a ready-made computer program that utilizies the formal solution method.

Optimal Program

Point C in Figure 3 represents the optimal solution that was found by inspection. The next step is to compute the program, i.e., the values of the variables. We can find the values for x_1 and x_2 by observing that point C is a point where the line $x_1 = 6$ cuts the line $300x_1 + 200x_2 = 2\ 400$. In order to find the values for x_1 and x_2 we must solve the set of two linear equations in two unknowns:

$$300x_1 + 200x_2 = 2\ 400$$
$$x_1 \qquad = \qquad 6$$

The solution is

$$x_1 = 6 \text{ and } x_2 = 3.$$

In the optimal program we produce 6 units of product A and 3 units of product B. The value of the objective function in the optimal solution gives the total contribution of the program. This value is found by substituting the values of x_1 and x_2 into the objective function

$$Z' = 600x_1' + 200x_2' = 600(6) + 200(3) = \$\ 4\ 200.$$

We conclude that in the planning situation represented by the model
it is optimal to the firm to produce both products in quantities given by
the optimal program and that this program will bring a total contribution
of $\$\ 4\ 200$.

An optimal program of a linear programming problem is the list of
the variables which are nonzero in the solution and the values of these
variables. (In special cases some variables in the program may be
zero but these special cases will not be analyzed in the present text.)
In the present example the firm will produce both products, i.e., both
x_1 and x_2 are nonzero in the optimal solution. In general, we cannot
expect that all variables of the problem will be nonzero. On the contrary,
in a planning situation where the firm has many products, it is most
likely that some products will not appear in the optimal program, i.e.,
the respective variables are zeros.

There are as many variables in a solution to a linear programming
problem as there are constraints in the problem, apart from the nonnegativity constraints. There are four such constraints in our example.
It follows that we should have four variables in the optimal program.
So far we have listed only two variables, x_1 and x_2. The apparent
contradiction comes from the fact that we have not utilized a formal
solution procedure but obtained the solution with an intuitive method.
The solution to this problem presented in the appendix lists four
variables.

When a general linear programming problem is solved the restrictions
must first be transformed into equalities. This is done by adding to the
inequalities so-called <u>slack variables</u>. In order to get a feeling about
the nature and use of these variables we convert the inequalities (1 - 2)
to (1 - 4) to equalities by adding the slack variables y_1, y_2, y_3, and y_4
in the following way:

$$
\begin{aligned}
x_1 \qquad\quad + y_1 \qquad\qquad\qquad &= \quad 6 \\
x_2 \qquad\quad + y_2 \qquad\qquad &= \quad 10 \\
10x_1 + 20x_2 \qquad\quad + y_3 \qquad &= \quad 160 \\
300x_1 + 200x_2 \qquad\qquad + y_4 &= 2\ 400
\end{aligned}
$$

A single slack variable is added to each inequality. The variable y_1
represents the slack between the maximum sales possibilities of product
A, 6, and the actual production, x_1. We have already solved the problem
and we know that the production of product A is 6 units. By substitution

we can now find the value for y_1:

$$6 + y_1 = 6,$$

or

$$y_1 = 6 - 6 = 0.$$

In this example there will be no slack between the production of A and its maximum sales possibilities.

The second slack variable y_2 represents the unutilized sales possibilities of product B. When we substitute the value of x_2 into the second equation we get value of y_2:

$$3 + y_2 = 10,$$

or

$$y_2 = 10 - 3 = 7.$$

We can now see that the slack variable associated with the sales constraint of product B is in the optimal program, and its value is 7. Substitution of the values of x_1 and x_2 into the third constraint gives the value of y_3:

$$10(6) + 20(3) + y_3 = 160,$$

or $\quad y_3 = 160 - 60 - 60 = 40.$

The slack variable y_3 which is associated with the capacity constraint has the value 40. The interpretation is that 40 hours of production capacity will be unutilized in the optimal program.

Substitution of the values for x_1 and x_2 into the fourth equation gives the value for the fourth slack variable, y_4:

$$300(6) + 200(3) + y_4 = 2\ 400,$$

$$y_4 = 0.$$

The variable y_4 represents the cash that is unutilized in the optimal program. This is cash in the excess of the required minimum balance of $ 500 which was built into the constraint (1 - 4). If the variable y_4 were at a positive value, it would indicate that more than $ 500 remains in the form of cash at the end of the period. Since $y_4 = 0$, we know that all available cash is being employed by production and sales.

When we observe the values of the slack variables, we can see that there are four variables altogether in the optimal program:

$$x_1 = 6,$$
$$x_2 = 3,$$

and

$$y_2 = 7,$$
$$y_3 = 40.$$

It is no coincidence that the slack variables associated with the first sales constraint and the cash constraint are zeros. We recall that point C is the intersection of these two constraints. The sales possibilities of product A are fully utilized. Similarly, all the financing possibilities are used. This is indicated by the fact that the values of the slack variables associated with these constraints are zeros. On the other hand, the sales possibilities of product B are not fully utilized. Similarly, there is unutilized production capacity. The same interpretation holds true in a general linear programming problem. If a slack variable is in the optimal program at a positive level, this indicates that the respective constraint is not binding in the optimal solution. A zero value for a slack variable again implies that the respective constraint is binding.

The slack variables do not appear in the objective function. Another way of saying this is to state that the coefficients of the slack variables in the objective function are all zeros. The contribution will not increase if the sales possibilities are unutilized or if the production capacity is not in full use. The objective function (1 - 1) could be written in the form:

$$Z = 300x_1 + 200x_2 + 0y_1 + 0y_2 + 0y_3 + 0y_4$$

without changing the original problem.

Most commercial computer programs automatically add the necessary slack variables to a problem. The computer output then lists in the optimal program as many variables as there are constraints in the problem. So does the program utilized in Appendix, for example. It is normal that some of these variables may be slack variables. We must therefore know the meaning of slack variables even though we do not go through the formal solution procedure in the present text.

Generation of Budgets on the Basis of Optimal Program

Based on the optimal solution we can now develop the projected cash flow as well as the projected financial statements. The projected cash flow is easily developed since there is only a single period in the present example. In real planning situations it is normal to divide the total planning period into subperiods and develop a cash flow projection for each subperiod while a single income statement is developed for the total planning period. The same procedure will be followed in later chapters also in this text.

The cash budget of the present example includes the following items:

Cash receipts			
Beginning cash balance			$ 1 000
Accounts receivable balance		6 800	
Sales of the period			
A: $(0)900x_1 =$	0		
B: $(0.5)800x_2 = 400(3) =$	1 200	1 200	8 000
Cash available			9 000
Cash Disbursements			
Production			
A: $300x_1 = 300(6) =$	1 800		
B: $600x_2 = 600(3) =$	1 800	3 600	
Fixed cash disbursements			
Accounts payable balance	900		
Repayment of loans	2 100		
Fixed expenses	1 900	4 900	8 500
Ending Cash Balance		$	500

Table 1-1. Cash Budget.

The projected income statement is developed on the basis of the optimal production and sales program and the fixed cost budget:

		Total	**Product A**	**Product B**
Sales, $		7 800	$900(6) = 5 400$	$800(3) = 2 400$
Less: Variable Costs		3 600	$300(6) = 1 800$	$600(3) = 1 800$
Contribution Margin		4 200	3 600	600
Less: Fixed Expenses				
Depreciation	500			
Payable in Cash	1 900			
Accruals	800	3 200		
Net Operating Profit		1 000		

Table 1-2. Projected Income Statement.

In order to develop the projected balance sheet we must take the beginning balance sheet and make adjustments to it based on the optimal program.

Assets				Liabilities			
Current Assets							
Cash		500		Short-term			
Accounts Receivable				Accounts Payable		800	
A: (1)900(6) =	5 400			Short-term Debt			
B: (0.5)800(3) =	1 200	6 600		Beginning			
Inventories		6 000	13 100	balance	10 000		
Fixed Assets				Repayments	2 100	7 900	8 700
Beginning Balance		4 500		Equity			
Depreciation		500	4 000	Beginning balance		7 400	
			$ 17 100	Profit for the period		1 000	8 400
							$ 17 100

Table 1-3. Projected Balance Sheet.

The ending balance of cash is stated in the cash budget. To set up the cash budget we had to compute the cash receipts resulting from the planned sales. Accounts receivable at the end of the period is given by the difference between the total sales revenue and the cash collections from it. Since nothing was collected from the sales of product A, its total sales remain in the accounts receivable. One half of the sales revenue of product B was collected during the period and another 50 percent remain in the accounts receivable. Production and sales were assumed to be equal. This implies that there is no change in inventories and the beginning balance figure of $ 6 000 is transferred to the projected ending balance. A $ 500 depreciation of fixed assets takes place during the planning period.

All variable production costs are paid in cash and therefore there is no ending balance of accounts payable resulting from raw material purchases. The only item in the accounts payable is the $ 800 accrual of fixed expenses. The balance of short-term debt is reduced by the repayment of $ 2 100 during the period. Equity is increased by the profit for the period.

The associated sales, production, and purchasing budgets can be derived from the optimal program. The sales budget is the following:

Product	Price	Quantity	$
A	900.–	6	5 400.–
B	800.–	3	2 400.–
			7 800.–

Table 1-4. The Sales Budget.

The production budget is simply the values of the variables x_1 and x_2. The purchasing budget can be developed by multiplying the values of the variables x_1 and x_2 by the standard amounts of raw materials used for making the respective product. In this example the usage of raw material equals the raw material purchases since we assume no change in inventories. In later examples we will let the raw material usage differ from the raw material purchases but then we will need separate variables for the usage and purchases.

Analysis of Shadow Prices

For every linear programming problem of the form

$$\text{Maximize } Z = c_1 x_1 + c_2 x_2$$

subject to

$$a_{11} x_1 + a_{12} x_2 \leq b_1$$

$$a_{21} x_1 + a_{22} x_2 \leq b_2$$

and

$$x_1 \geq 0, \ x_2 \geq 0,$$

there is another linear programming problem called its dual. We note that in the original problem we are <u>maximizing</u> the objective function subject to constraints which are all (apart from the nonnegativity constraints) of the form <u>less than or equal to</u>. The dual problem is of the form:

$$\text{Minimize } E = b_1 u_1 + b_2 u_2$$

subject to

$$a_{11} u_1 + a_{21} u_2 \geq x_1$$

$$a_{12} u_1 + a_{22} u_2 \geq x_2$$

and

$$u_1 \geq 0, \ u_2 \geq 0.$$

The dual problem has been derived by selecting a variable for each constraint of the original problem. In our example, the variable u_1 is associated with the constraint $a_{11} x_1 + a_{12} x_2 \leq b_1$ and the variable u_2 with the constraint $a_{21} x_1 + a_{22} x_2 \leq b_2$. The objective function of the dual is formulated by multiplying the coefficients on the right hand side of the original problem by the dual variables accociated with the restrictions and by minimizing the sum of these terms. Finally we take the columns of the original problem and develop the constraints of the dual. For example, the x_1-column of the original problem results in the following constraint:

$$a_{11}u_1 + a_{21}u_2 \geqq c_1$$

The coefficient of the objective function of the original problem, c_1, is now the right-hand side constant of the dual constraint and the inequality sign is of the form <u>greater than or equal to.</u>

If a constraint of the original problem is not of the required form, we must first convert it to the required form. For example, if the first constraint of the original problem had been

$$a_{11}x_1 + a_{12}x_2 \geqq b_1,$$

we should have converted it into the required form by multiplying its both sides by (-1):

$$-a_{11}x_1 - a_{12}x_2 \leqq -b_1.$$

It has been proved that a number of relations hold between the original problem and its dual. These relations can be utilized in order to analyze the solution of the original problem or even to solve the original problem. We do not attempt to go through the proof of the dual theorem in the present text. Instead, we merely state some of the relationships that will be used in the remaining part of this text.

First of these relationships states that the optimal value of the objective function of the original problem is equal to the optimal value of the objective function of the dual problem. If we know the solution of one of the problems, then we immediatelly know also the value of the objective function of the other problem. We know this without having to solve the other problem. Moreover, if we know the dimension of the objective function of the original problem (e.g., dollars), then we automatically know the dimension of the objective function of the dual problem.

In addition, if a variable of the original problem is in the optimal program, then the values of the variables of the dual problem are such that the respective constraint is an equality. For example, if x_1 in our original problem is positive in the optimal solution, then the variables u_1 and u_2 take values such that the constraint

$$a_{11}u_1 + a_{21}u_2 = c_1$$

is an equality. Conversely, if we know that a constraint of the dual problem is satisfied as a strict inequality, then the corresponding variable of the original problem is not in the optimal program.

If the variables of the original problem take values such that in the optimal solution the left-hand side of a constraint is less than the right-hand side, then the dual variable associated with this constraint is zero in the optimal solution of the dual problem. On the other hand, if the variables of the original problem take values such that the left-hand side of a constraint is equal to the right-hand side, then the respective dual variable is larger than (or, in a special case, equal to) zero.

Let us consider the problem (1 - 1) to (1 - 5) and formulate its dual. The original problem is a maximization problem. All the constraints are of the type where the left-hand side must be less than or equal to the right-hand side. We can therefore directly write the dual problem. We choose the dual variables u_1, u_2, u_3 and u_4 such that the first variable is associated with the first marketing constraint of (1 - 2), the second variable with the second marketing constraint, etc. We get the following dual problem

$$\text{Minimize } E = 6u_1 + 10u_2 + 160u_3 + 2400u_4$$

subject to

$$u_1 \quad + 10u_3 + 200u_4 \geqq 600$$
$$u_2 + 20u_3 + 200u_4 \geqq 200$$

and

$$u_1, u_2, u_3, u_4 \geqq 0.$$

The optimal value of the objective function of the original problem is $ 4 200. According to the dual theorem, we then know that

$$E' = 6u_1' + 10u_2' + 160u_3' + 2\,400u_4' = \$\ 4\ 200.$$

Furthermore, we can find out the dimensions of the dual variables. The coefficient of the first variable is 6 units of product. Since the product of this coefficient and the variable u_1 is dollars, we know that the dimension of the variable u_1 must be $/unit of product. Similarly, the dimension of the variable u_2 must be $/unit of product. The coefficient of the third variable is 160 hours. It follows that the dimension of u_3 must be $/hour. Finally, the dimension of the last variable u_4 must be $/$.

Both x_1 and x_2 are in the optimal program of the original problem. The respective dual constraints must therefore be equalities

$$u_1 \quad + 10u_3 + 300u_4 = 600$$

$$u_2 \quad + 20u_3 + 200u_4 = 200.$$

Without further information we cannot find the values of the dual variables since we have four unknowns in two equations. We must use the relationship according to which the dual variable is zero if the respective constraint of the original problem is a strict inequality. Using this relationship we can eliminate two unknowns. Since the second marketing constraint was not effectively binding in the optimal solution, the respective dual variable is zero:

$$u_2 = 0.$$

In the same way we can deduce that the dual variable associated with the capacity constraint is zero:

$$u_3 = 0.$$

After these reductions we have two equations in two unknowns:

$$u_1 \quad + 300u_4 = 600$$
$$200u_4 = 200.$$

Solving these equations we get the values of the remaining two variables

$$u_1 = 300 \ \$/\text{unit},$$
$$u_4 = \quad 1 \ \$/\$.$$

We can finally check whether the values of the objective functions of the two problems are equal:

$$E' = 6(300) + 10(0) + 160(0) + 2\ 400(1) = 4\ 200 = Z.$$

The dual variables are called the shadow prices of the constraints of the original problem. For example, u_1, is the shadow price associated with the first marketing constraint. These shadow prices have a large information content. We can use them to analyze changes in the value of the objective function of the original problem that result from changes in the conditions under which the original problem was formulated.

In our example, the shadow price associated with the first marketing constraint, u_1. tells us that the total contribution will increase $ 300 if the constant on the right-hand side of the restriction $x_1 \leq 6$ is increased by one unit. In other words, if we can somehow increase the demand of product A by one unit and if we adjust our plans optimally to this change in the conditions underlying the planning, the total contribution will increase $ 300.

In order to see the validity of this statement we solve the resulting new problem. This has been done in Figure 4. The new problem is in all other respects alike the problem (1 - 1) to (1 - 5) except that now the first marketing constraint is $x_1 \leq 7$. The right-hand side constant has been increased by one unit.

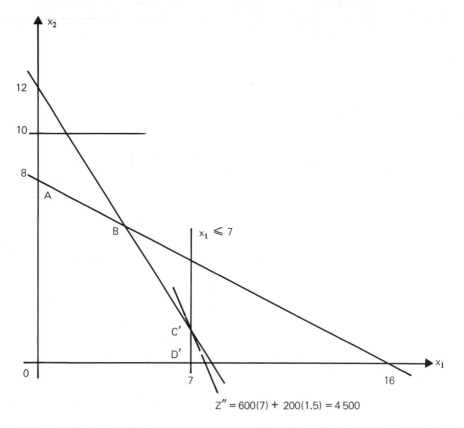

$$Z'' = 600(7) + 200(1.5) = 4\,500$$

Figure 4. The change in the value of the objective function that results from a change in the right-hand side constant.

Point C´ gives now the optimal solution. This point is the intersection of the lines $300x_1 + 200x_2 = 2\,400$ and $x_1 = 7$. Finding the coordinates of point C´ gives the new optimal program:

$$x_1 = 7$$
$$x_2 = 1.5.$$

26

Substitution of these values into the objective function gives the new optimum:

$$Z'' = 600(7) + 200(1.5) = \$\ 4\ 500.$$

Taking the difference between the original and new optimums shows that the value of the objective function has increased by the exact amount of the shadow price:

$$Z'' - Z' = 4\ 500 - 4\ 200 = 300 = u_1.$$

The shadow price associated with the second marketing constraint is zero: $u_2 = 0$. The shadow price gives the same information that can be deduced from Figure 3. If the right-hand side constant of the second marketing constraint is increased by one unit, i.e., if the new constraint is $x_2 \leq 11$, the optimal solution remains unchanged and ther is no increase in the total contribution. In the same way, the shadow price associated with the capacity constraint indicates that an increase of one hour in production capacity would not increase the total contribution: $u_3 = 0$. If an additional dollar is made available, for example by reducing the required minimum ending cash balance, which implies that the right-hand side constant of the liquidity constraint increases from $\$\ 2\ 400$ to $\$\ 2\ 401$, then the total contribution is increased by one dollar: $u_4 = 1$. Instead of a reduction in the minimum ending balance we might consider a new loan. The shadow price tells us that in this example we could pay almost a 100 per cent interest on the loan and still make a profit. For example, an interest of 90 per cent per period would leave us an increase of $u_4 - 0.9 = \$\ 0.1$ in the total contribution.

The shadow prices are valid only on given conditions. The first condition is that a change must take place only in one right-hand side constant at a time. All the other constants must remain unchanged. Secondly, the solution must be optimally adjusted to the change that takes place. We remember from Figure 4 that an increase in the sales possibilities of product A by one unit caused a change in the production of both products. The value of the variable x_1 was increased from 6 to 7 and the value of x_2 was decreased from 3 to 1.5. These changes explain why we could not tell the increase in the total contribution directly by looking at the unit contribution of product A. The net increase in the total contribution was $\$\ 300$ and not $\$\ 600$ which is the unit contribution of product A. This came from the fact that the production of B was simultaneously reduced. The third condition for the validity of the shadow prices is that the increase in the right-hand side constant must be so small that the same variables are still in the optimal program after the necessary adjustments are made. The values of the variables can change but they must still be in the optimal program. For example, if the right-hand side constant of the marketing restriction of product A increases by 3 units, i.e., if the new constraint is $x_1 \leq 9$, then Figure 4 shows that point C′ moves to the x_1-axis at the point $x_1 = 8$ and the last unit increase in the constant will not increase the contribution. The effect of the change can no longer be evaluated with the help of the shadow price alone. The shadow prices must therefore not be interpreted without reservations. However, in large problems they direct attention to changes that are worth a further analysis.

According to their definition, the shadow prices indicate the increase in the value of the objective function that results from a one unit increase in right-hand side constant. However, with reservations we can analyze the joint effects of several shadow prices simultaneously. As an example, let us consider the question whether it would pay to the firm represented by the model (1 - 1) to (1 - 5) to use some of its scarce funds for an advertizing campaign directed for increasing the sales possibilities of product A. Let us assume that the marketing management has estimated that a campaign costing $ 100 would increase the demand of product A by one unit. Would it be worth while to engage in this campaign?

To find the answer we must think about all changes that result in the optimal program. First of all, using $ 100 for an advertizing campaign will reduce the right-hand side constant of the cash constraint. It now becomes

$$300x_1 + 200x_2 \leq 2\ 300.$$

The effect of the change in the right-hand side constant can be analyzed with the help of the shadow price u_4. The total contribution will be reduced by $100u_4 = \$ 100$. In addition, we must remember that spending $ 100 for an advertizing campaign will directly reduce the contribution by that amount. The profit is thus reduced in two ways. Firstly, there is the indirect reduction which is the result of not having the funds available for financing the operations. Secondly, there is the direct reduction resulting from the increase in expenses.

On the other hand, the increase in the sales possibilities of product A will increase the contribution u_1 dollars. The total net effect of all these changes is the sum of the terms:

The increase in profit resulting from the increase in the sales possibilities of product A	$u_1 =$		$ 300
Less: The decrease in profit resulting from the advertizing campaign			
Reduction in the right-hand side constant of the liquidity constraint	$100u_4 =$	100	
Increase in advertizing costs		100	200
The net change (= increase in profit)			$ 100

28

It appears that in this example it is advisable to use some of the scarce funds for an advertizing campaign because the net effect is favorable. If we analyze Figure 4, it can be seen that this time the changes in both constraints are so small that the analysis of shadow prices gives the correct answer.

The Simplex Method and the Shadow Prices

The oldest and best known method of solving general linear programming problems is the simplex method which was developed in the 1940s. We will not cover the method in this text but assume that the problems are solved using a computer. However, it is worth noting that the simplex method (and the related other solution methods that have been later developed) generates the shadow prices simultaneously with the solution of the original problem.

The computer codes utilized for solving the sample problem also generate the shadow prices associated with the optimal program. (See the Appendix). If we use these codes for solving the problems presented int the text we do not have to worry about the generation of the shadow prices. The preceding analysis is only meant to give the reader a feeling about the relationships between the shadow prices and the original problem.

Problems

1 - 1. The company produces a single product in two plants. The product is sold in a single market with a limited demand. The sales price is $ 17/unit of product. The variable costs of production are $ 9/unit in plant A and $ 8/unit in plant B. Marketing management estimates that the demand will not exceed 30 000 units. A unit of product made in plant A requires 2.4 hours of production capacity. The capacity available in plant A is 30 000 hours. The capacity required per unit of product is 1.5 hours and the total capacity is 20 000 hours in plant B.

Formulate the problem of the contribution maximization as a linear programming problem.

1 - 1. Consider a firm which produces two products, A and B, in a

single plant. The products are sold in two marketing areas which are called the Northern and Southern District. The following estimates are available about the demand, the sales prices and the variable selling costs of the products.

	Sales Districts			
	Southern		Northern	
	Products		Products	
	A	B	A	B
Sales price, $/unit	12,-	17.-	13.-	18.-
Selling costs, $/unit	4,-	3.-	5.-	4.-
Sales limits, units	4 000	6 000	2 000	5 000

The total production capacity of the plant is 30 000 hours. The variable manufacturing costs and the capacity required per unit of product are as follows.

	Product A	Product B
Capacity required, h./unit	1.5	2.-
Variable mfg costs, $/unit	6.-	10.-

Formulate the problem of the maximization of the contribution as a linear programming problem.

1 - 3. Assume that the firm manufactures and sells two products, x_1 and x_2, with a unit contribution of \$ 3.- and \$ 2.-, respectively. The sales of product x_1 cannot exceed 8 units. There is no upper limit of the sales of product x_2, but it must exceed 4 units. The production is limited by the available capacity which is 24 hours. Product x_1 requires 2 hours/unit and product x_2 3 hours/unit of capacity. We get the following problem:

$$\text{Maximize } Z = 3x_1 + 2x_2$$

subject to

$$x_1 \leq 8$$
$$x_2 \geq 4$$
$$2x_1 + 3x_2 \leq 24$$

and

$$x_1 \geq 0, \ x_2 \geq 0.$$

Required:
a) Solve the problem with the graphic method and indicate the maximum contribution as well as the optimal program.
b) Solve the shadow prices associated with the optimum solution using the relations between the original problem and its dual.
c) How much will the total contribution change and in which direction if the right-hand side constant of the constraint $x_2 \geq 4$ is reduced by one unit?

1 - 4. Consider the sample problem (1 - 1) to (1 - 5). How will the solution space be altered if there is an additional marketing constraint which requires that the production and sales of product B must be at least 80 per cent of the production and sales of product A:

$$x_2 \geq 0.8x_1.$$

Required:
a) Find the optimum solution to the new problem.
b) Indicate the constraints that effectively bind the new optimum solution.
c) Compute the shadow prices associated with these constraints.
d) If the new marketing constraint requires that, instead of 80 per cent, the product mix must contain at least 33 per cent of product B of the amount of product A, then what is the solution space, the optimal program, and the shadow prices associated with this program?

1 - 5. Consider a firm that produces two products, A and B, in two plants. The plants are identified with the subscripts K and L. Both products are sold in two marketing areas that are identified with subscripts N and S. Upper limits of demand, sales prices, variable selling costs, and the costs of transporting the products from the plants to the marketing areas are listed in the following table.

	Marketing Areas			
	N		S	
	Products		Products	
	A	B	A	B
Upper limits of sales, units	9 000	12 000	7 500	6 000
Selling prices, $/unit	12.–	17.–	13.–	18.–
Variable selling costs, $/unit	4.–	5.–	3.–	4.–
Cost of transportation, $/unit				
Plant K	1.–	1.–	2.–	2.–
Plant L	2.–	2.–	1.–	1.–

The parts for both products are made in each plant in a common machining department. The assembly of the products is carried out in separate assembly departements. Both machining and assembly capacity is available only in limited quantities in each plant. Variable manufacturing costs, the required capacity, and the total available capacity are the following.

	Plants			
	K		L	
	Products		Products	
	A	B	A	B
Variable mfg. costs, $/unit	5.-	6.-	4.-	5.-
Capacity required, h/unit				
Assembly				
Product A	1.5	–	1	–
Product B	–	2	–	2
Machining	3	2	2.5	1.5
Capacity available, hours				
Assembly				
Product A	12 000		8 000	
Product B	–	16 000	–	22 000
Machining	30 000		40 000	

Required:
a) Formulate a linear programming problem with the objective of the maximization of the difference between the sales revenue and the variable selling, transportation, and manufacturing costs subject to the demand, assembly, and machining constraints.
b) Solve the problem with computer. Prepare sales, transportation, and production budgets for the marketing areas and the plants.
c) Analyze with the help of the shadow prices associated with the optimal solution the most important factors that the management should pay attention to. Should the management concentrate on increasing the sales of a product in a given area, or should it concentrate on removing the production bottlenecks?

1 – 6. SKIMOTOR, INC. is a company making snowmobiles and outboard motors which sells its products through large chain stores. The size of the company is small compared to the total market of these products and the products are of a high technical quality. For these reasons the company has not experienced marketing difficulties previously and does not expect them in the future selling season for which the plans are now under consideration. Since the two products have different peak seasons and are being sold to different kinds of customers there are no interdependences between the sales of the two products.

Production is carried out in a single plant. Parts for each product are first manufactured in the machining department after which they move to the assembly line. The standard machining time for the parts of the snowmobile is 10 hours per unit of product. An outboard motor requires instead 30 hours of machining time. Standard hours have been developed also for the assembly operation. A snowmobile requires 20 hours and an outboard motor 20 hours of assembly time. The total capacity of the machining department is 150 hours. It is estimated that the assembly department has a capacity òf 200 hours.

The sales price of snowmobiles is $ 1 200. It can be assumed that on the average one third of the sales revenue is collected during the same period the sales take place and the remainder in the following period. Outboard motors are being sold at a price of $ 1 000 per unit and 20 per cent of the sales revenue is collected during the same period, the rest being received one period after.

Standard variable manufacturing costs are as follows

	Snowmobile	Outboard motor
Direct wages and variable overhead, $/unit		
Assembly	200.–	100.–
Machining	100.–	300.–
Raw materials and parts, $/unit	700.–	300.–
	1 000.–	700.–

Cash payments for direct wages and variable overhead are made at the same rate at which production proceeds. Parts and raw materials of outboard motors are also paid in cash at the rate they are used in production. The terms of payment for the parts and raw materials of snowmobiles are such that about $ 400 per unit is paid during the same period the product is made and the remainder in the following period.

The financial position of the company at the beginning of the planning period is represented by the following beginning balance sheet:

Beginning Balance Sheet

Cash	600	Accounts Payable	3 000
Accounts Receivable	9 000	Term Loan	10 300
Inventories	3 200	Equity	4 500
Fixed Assets	5 000		
	$ 17 800		$ 17 800

It is estimated that the accounts receivable balance is collected during the planning period in total. Inventories are expected to remain at their present level. Depreciation of fixed assets is $ 400 and fixed expenses payable in cash are $ 600. Accounts payable balance must be paid in total during the period. Repayment of term loan is $ 400. The firm attempts to gain a better liquidity and therefore the management wants the cash ending balance increase at least at the level of $ 800.

33

We have been requested to develop a complete budget for the planning period consisting of sales-, production-, purchasing-, and cash budgets as well as projected financial statements. The management is also interested in knowing whether it would pay to transfer workers from one production department to the other if there is imbalance between the capacities of the two departments. A transfer of 50 production hours from the assembly to the machining department could be made but this would involve a retraining cost of $ 1 200 which would have to be expensed in total during the planning period.

2 Single Period Budget Models

A Single Plant Model

Weaknesses in the Traditional Budgeting Process

Traditionally the budget is built along functional lines. A typical procedure is to develop sales, inventory, production, purchasing, cash, capital expenditure, as well as research and development budgets which are then assembled into a master budget together with projected financial statements.

When separate functional budgets are analyzed in isolation they may appear to be quite reasonable and possible to carry out. Only when we begin to set up a master budget it may turn out that the functional budgets are incompatible. The program of a single function cannot be determined in isolation. We must take into account that the firm is a system with a number of interdependent functions.

In traditional budgeting this problem is solved by beginning the budgeting procedure with a given function and then adjusting the other functional budgets to it. Most authors state that the sales budget must be taken as a starting point and the other budgets must be adjusted to it. Other authors are of the opinion that the cash budget is the most important. Sometimes the production budget is taken as the basis of the budgeting procedure. A common feature of all these approaches is that a functional budget is more or less arbitrarily selected as a starting point and all other budgets adjusted to it.

To select a single functional budget is correct if that budget binds the operations of the firm before any other budget does. The difficulty with this approach is that, in general, it is impossible to know in advance which functional budget will be critical in the optimal solution. It is normal that when we begin to collect data for the functional budgets, there appear to be several potential bottlenecks.

Figure 5 represents the most common budgeting procedure where we start with the sales budget and move to production, purchasing, and cash budgets. The sales budget is first developed on the basis of demand data and the sales forecasting rules applied to this data. The sales budget and the beginning balances of the finished products are then used to develop the production budget. The capacity required by the planned production is compared to the available capacity. If the available capacity exceeds the required capacity or is equal to it, we can consider the production budget to be final and move to the next functional budget. If the available capacity is less than the required capacity we must return back to the sales budget and leave out enough products to bring the required capacity to the level of the available capacity. In this process we try to leave out products which require a lot of production capacity in relation to the contribution that they give.

When the sales and production budgets are adjusted to each other we can prepare the budgets for the service departments. Furthermore, we can take the planned production and explode it into parts and raw material requirements. The parts and raw materials required by the production and the beginning balances of parts and raw materials are next used to develop the required purchases of parts and raw materials. When we add to these purchases the supplies needed by the various production and service departments we can develop the purchasing budget.

Starting from the financial position represented by the beginning balance and taking into account the effects of sales, production, service department, and purchasing budgets as well as from capital expenditure and research and development budgets we can figure out the financing needs for the period. The financing requirements are then compared to the available financing. If the available financing does not cover the needs we must return back to the sales budget and revise it by excluding products which tie up considerable amount of funds in relation to their contribution. Then we must revise the remaining functional budgets to bring them in line with the revised sales budget.

We have excluded from Figure 5 a number of other possibilities to reduce the financing needs. We have implicitly assumed that the capital budget as well as the research and development budget have been developed independently of the other functional budgets. A possibility to reduce the required financing is to decrease the planned investments in capital assets, or make cuts in the R & D budget. Another possibility is to decrease the planned ending balances of finished products, parts, and raw materials.

When the functional plans have been adjusted to the available financing we can finally compute the projected income statement and the projected balance sheet. If the planned profit is not satisfactory in relation to the capital employed in operations we must return back to some functional

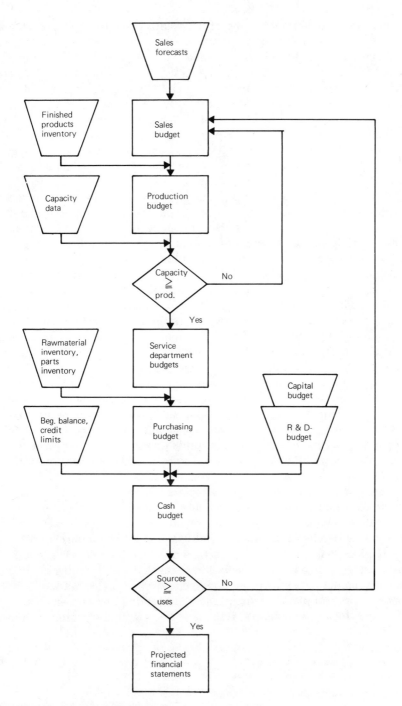

Figure 5. Traditional Budgeting Process.

budget, revise it to improve the profit position and then go through a chain of revisions in other functional budgets. The various possibilities for these revisions have been excluded from Figure 5. The approach presented in Figure 5 would produce an optimal budget only in the case where we do not need to return back to earlier stages. This would be an exceptional case, however. It is normal that in planning which takes place in several stages we must go through several loops. This makes the finding of an optimal master plan a very difficult, if not impossible, task because we cannot cancel all previous plans because of the large amount of work involved. Instead, we must limit the revisions to specific areas of the functional plans.

These difficulties have led to the realization that in order to develop an optimal master plan we must develop the functional budgets simultaneously instead of developing them in successive steps. From the master plan based on the simultaneous solution we can then derive the functional budgets which are all compatible with each other. The development of budget models has moved into this direction in the past few years. Instead of production oriented "plant models" we must develop models that integrate all the major functions of the firm which are then used as a basis of budgets. This integration brings the planning approach close to the level of top management because top management has traditionally been the point in organization where the viewpoints of different functional managers have been reconciled.

In the present text we will gradually move towards the complicated planning situations of real firms. In this section we consider a simple planning situation where the firm under analysis sells a very limited product mix in a single market and produces these products in a single plant. There are only two products in the product mix. The structure of the products is also very simple. Another very important simplification is that our planning horizon consists of a single period.

Compared to the introductory example of the first chapter we are now facing a more complicated planning situation, however. We will drop the assumption that sales must equal production. Similarly, we will not require that the raw material usage must equal purchases. This implies that we must select different variables for sales, production and purchases. In addition, we will assume that the financing decisions are more complicated than in the introductory example. We will approach the real planning situations by assuming that the firm can obtain additional financing by taking new loans within given credit lines.

Data Collection

The maximum demand of the various products must be estimated just like in the traditional budgeting process. However, we now estimate the sales potential only without assuming that all demand can be satisfied, or that it is profitable to sell all products that could be sold. We assume that the marketing management has analyzed the demand conditions and has come up with the conclusion that the upper limits of the sales of the two products are as shown in Table 2-1. The table shows also the estimated sales prices.

Product	Selling price, $/unit	Selling possibilities, units
A	3.50	250 000
B	4.50	300 000

Table 2-1. Demand of the Products.

The demand of the two products is assumed to be independent of each other. As a result of this assumption it is possible that the optimal solution will include the sales and production of a single product. In practice, the builders of budget models try to achieve a balanced product mix by setting lower limits to the sales of the products. This ensures that at least the amount required by the lower limit is produced and sold of each product. However, it is questionable whether such lower limits should be used to begin with. It may be better to find an optimal solution without any lower limits and let the marketing management evaluate the solution. If some products are missing that in the opinion of the marketing management should be produced and sold, then we can add the lower limits to these products and generate an optimal solution to the revised model. The difference between the values of the objective function in the two solutions tells us how much the company loses because it keeps given products in its sales mix. If the loss is considerable, this may lead the marketing management to consider ways for improving the situation. Some of these possibilities are changes in the sales prices of the unprofitable products, purchasing these products from other firms instead of making them, or discontinuing the marketing efforts of the products either directly or by the way of not rewarding the sales organization for the sales of these prodcuts. In line with this argument we are not considering any lower limits of sales in the present example.

Table 2-2 presents the capacity data. We are assuming that the production capacity is of a single dimension which is a drastic simplification of real planning situations where we may have to consider tens or hundreds of different capacity groups. In later examples we will move towards greater realism also in this respect. Also, we do not consider the possibility of overtime or a second shift in the present example, although these alternatives may be relevant in actual planning and can be taken into account in modeling. The total available production capacity is assumed to be 285 000 hours.

Required capacity, h./unit		Available capacity, hours
Product A	Product B	
0.5	0.6	285 000

Table 2-2. The required capacity by products and the total available capacity.

Product	Production	Desired Ending Inventory, units	Beginning Inventory, units
A	y_A	25 000	30 000
B	y_B	28 000	18 000

Table 2-3. Desired ending inventory and available beginning inventory of finished products, units.

Raw material	Usage, unit/ unit of product	Total amount used	Desired ending balance	Beginning balance	Price, $/unit
W	3	$3y_A$	55 000	45 000	0.15
U	2	$2y_B$	80 000	90 000	0.265

Table 2-4. The usage and the inventories of raw materials.

Cost item	Product A	Product B
Direct materials		
3 units of material W à $ 0.15	0.45	–
2 » » U à $ 0.265	–	0.53
Direct Wages		
0.5 hours à $ 1.80	0.90	–
0.6 » à $ 1.80	–	1.08
Variable overhead, $ 1.–/direct labor hour	0.50	0.60
Total variable costs, $/unit	1.85	2.21

Table 2-5. The variable costs of the products.

Table 2-3 presents the inventory budget of finished products. Since we are building a single period model it cannot take into account the possibility of manufacturing for stock in order to meet seasonal demand. This question will be brought under analysis in later models when we consider several periods with variations in demand. The model will then solve for the amounts of products to be kept in the inventory from one period to the next.

We assume that the beginning balance of product A is 30 000 units and that of product B 18 000 units. Because the operations of the firm are continued after the end of the planning period and because stocks are being held either to make the operations of one department independent of the others or to act as a buffer against uncertainty, the management wants to have a given level of inventories also at the end of the planning period. The inventory of product A can be reduced from its present level to 25 000 units. The ending inventory of product B must be at least 28 000 units which means an increase of 10 000 units from the present level.

The required ending inventories must be based on the subjective estimates of management. If the optimal solution indicates that we cannot meet all demand and if we have required that there must be given ending inventories this must not be interpreted to mean that we would not allow in reality the inventories to be reduced even to zero in order to satisfy the demand. As we will see later, it is not clear, however, which inventory should be reduced. If the solution indicates that demand exceeds capacity, it will also indicate the product whose ending balance should first be reduced. The ending inventory requirements attempt merely to take into account that in a going concern there are always a certain amount of inventories and that the management must evaluate their levels in any planning situation.

Many industrial products are made by first producing individual parts and then assembling the parts into the final products. A single unit of product may contain hundreds or even thousands of parts. The parts in turn may require a large number of different raw materials. Budget models cover such long time periods that it is out of question to include into the model a detailed production plan of individual parts. The detailed production planning must be carried out by another planning system which operates with a shorter horizon.

Even if the budget model cannot include detailed production planning we must develop a purchasing budget. This can be done, for example, by computing the amount of raw materials needed for the production of the final products. This is done by multiplying the amounts of final products in the production budget by their bills of material. The required amounts of raw materials are then multiplied by their standard costs. Table 2-4 presents the combined bill of materials for both products. In this example it is extremely simple because we assume

41

that only one type of raw materials is used for each product. The firm uses, in other words, only two kinds of raw materials.

We represent the amounts of the products to be made by the unknowns y_A and y_B as indicated in Table 2-3. Table 2-4 indicates that if we make one unit of product A, we must use three units of raw material W. The total amount of this material used is therefore $3y_A$. In the same way we note that the amount of raw material U used in the production of B is $2y_B$, because each unit of B requires 2 units of U.

Table 2-4 shows also the beginning balances and the desired ending balances of the raw materials. We note again that the ending balances are set up tentatively. If the solution shows that all the demand cannot be satisfied because of the lack of funds we may have to reduce the ending balances to save cash. The optimal solution will show which raw material balance is the first one to be reduced. Table 2-4 gives finally the standard costs of raw materials. These costs will be employed to develop the purchasing and cash budget as well as the projected income statement. For these and other reasons that will become apparent when we work through the remaining examples it is clear that te existence of a standard cost system is a factor which greatly simplifies the data collection work of budget models.

Table 2-5 presents the cost structure of the two products. We assume that the firm uses a variable standard cost system where only the variable costs are considered to be product costs. The costs for direct material must be consistent with the raw material usage. We assumed, for example, that the standard quantity of raw material W used for making product A is 3 units. The standard cost of raw material W is $ 0.15 per unit. The standard raw material cost of product A is therefore $ 0.45 per unit of product. Similarly, the standard labor costs of the products must be consistent with the required production capacities. According to Table 2-2 the required capacity of product A is 0.5 hours per unit. We assume that the capacity is measured with direct labor hours. Therefore, the standard labor cost of product A is the standard wage rate, $ 1.80 per hour, times the required capacity 0.5 hours per unit, or $ 0.90 per unit of product. The variable overhead costs are also assumed to be distributed on the basis of direct labor hours.

Table 2-6 shows the beginning balance of the firm. The beginning balances of cash and accounts receivable are available for the financing of operations. The dollar figures for inventory balances must again be consistent with the physical quantities presented in earlier tables. The beginning balances of raw materials in Table 2-4 have been multiplied by the standard prices of raw materials. Similarly, the beginning balances of finished products of Table 2-3 have been multiplied by the standard costs of Table 2-5. It is assumed that work in process remains at the level of the beginning balance during the period and therefore, we show only a dollar figure. This assumption allows us to simplify the model in that we can establish the relationship between the final products and the raw materials directly without having to first set up relations between the raw materials and work in process and then set up another set of relations between work in process and the final products.

The assets side of the balance sheet includes prepaid expenses in the amount of $ 6 200 and fixed assets of $ 1 058 220. No changes are assumed to take place with respect to prepaid expenses. The depreciation of fixed assets will be stated later on in connection with the budget for fixed expenses. Similarly, we assume that additions to the fixed assets, i.e., the capital budget, has been developed separately from the model and will be presented below. Its effect in the model will be limited to financing needs that it creates.

Assets			Liabilities		
Current Assets			Accounts Payable		
Cash	112 000		Raw Materials	38 000	
Accounts Receivable	110 000		Salaries and Wages	78 000	
Inventories			Taxes	55 000	
Raw Materials			Other	37 500	208 500
W 6 750			Long term Debt		100 000
U 23 850	30 600		Equity		
Work in Process	87 900		Shareholders' capital	900 000	
Finished Products			Undistributed profit	291 700	1 191 700
A 55 000					
B 39 780	95 280	435 780			
Prepaid Expenses		6 200			
Fixed Assets		1 058 220			
		$ 1 500 200			$ 1 500 200

Table 2-6. The Beginning Balance Sheet.

The first item on the liabilities side of the balance sheet, accounts payable balance resulting from raw material purchases, must be paid during the period. Accrued salaries and wages in the amount of $ 78 000 must also be paid. However, the work force is kept on an even level and accrued salaries and wages will therefore also remain constant from period to period. For this reason we assume later that all salaries and wages are paid currently and that the beginning balance of $ 78 000 also represents the ending balance. Accrued income tax of $ 55 000 must all be paid in the planning period. The projected income statement will show the new tax liability at the end of the period. Other accounts payable, $ 37 500, are assumed to remain at their previous level. The amount in the beginning balance can therefore be transferred to the projected balance sheet.

Long term debt will rquire two payments during the period, interest in the amount of $ 5 000 and a repayment of $ 10 000. These payments must be made regardless of other plans. The shareholders capital remains unchanged during the period. There will be a dividend distribution of $ 20 000 during the period. This will also involve a fixed cash payment. The projected net income will increase the undistributed profits in the projected balance sheet.

Table 2-7 shows finally the fixed selling, administration and manufacturing expenses. We are preparing a short-term plan and we can therefore assume that we are dealing with a going concern with fixed expenses that must be incurred regardless of other plans. We can therefore draw up the fixed costs budget before the solution to the model. The fixed costs are subdivided into depreciation and expenses that must be paid in cash. We assume in this model that all the costs payable in cash must be paid currently during the planning period. They must be included in the stage where we compute the fixed cash expenditure for the liquidity constraint.

Fixed Selling Expenses	
Depreciation	60 000
Payable in Cash	250 000
	$ 310 000
Fixed Administration Expenses	
Depreciation	50 000
Payable in Cash	290 000
	$ 340 000
Fixed Manufacturing Expenses	
Depreciation	110 000
Payable in Cash	155 000
	$ 265 000

Table 2-7. The fixed expenses budget.

Apart from the data presented in the previous tables we need additional information for the development of the model. The sales of the products involve the payment of two per cent commission to the distributors. These variable selling costs are observed in the objective. However, it is assumed that the payment of the commission takes place one period after. The commission will therefore not be reflected in the liquidity constraint for the period.

The beginning balance of accounts receivable will be collected during the period. According to the prevailing terms of payment, 90 per cent of the sales of product A are collected during the planning period. The respective percentage for product B is 95 per cent.

The beginning balance of accounts payable for raw materials is paid in total during the period. The purchases of raw material W involve a payment of 93 per cent and those of raw material U a payment of 85 per cent during the same period.

The minimum required ending cash balance is assumed to be $ 100 000.
The payment of interest and amortization of existing loans has already
been discussed above. New loans can be taken in a desired amount which
must not exceed the limit of $ 50 000. An interest of 10 per cent will be
calculated on the amount of new loans taken. However, the payment of
interest takes place one period later. The capital expenditure budget
involves a payment of $ 250 000 during the period.

Model Formulation

The following step in the procedure is the formulation of the budget
model on the basis of the preceding data. Since we are considering a
short-run plan, we take as the objective the maximization of the
difference between the sales revenue and the various variable costs.
In the present example we must consider variable selling, manufacturing
and financing costs. This objective is to be maximized subject to the
constraints implicit in the data of the preceding tables.
  The objective function can be presented as follows:

$$(2 - 1) \quad \text{Maximize } Z = (3.50 - 0.07 - 1.85)x_A + (4.50 - 0.09 - 2.21)x_B - r$$

The objective Z stands now for the difference between the sales
revenue and all variable costs, i.e., it is no longer the total contribution generated by the sales as in (1 - 1). The variable x_A represents
the sales of product A, x_B the sales of the product B, and r the interest
expense for the period. The variables representing the sales of the
products are multiplied by coefficients which have been obtained by
deducting from the sales price of the product its variable selling and
manufacturing costs. The variable selling costs are 2 per cent of the
respective selling prices. For example, the sales price of product A
is $ 3.5 per unit and its selling expenses are $ 0.07 per unit.
  The objective is to be achieved subject to various constraints. First
of all, we must observe the estimated maximum demand for both
products which was presented in Table 2 - 1:

$$(2 - 2) \quad x_A \leq 250\ 000,$$
$$x_B \leq 300\ 000.$$

The constraints require that the sales of both products must be less
than or equal to the estimated maximum demand of the respective

product. In the example of chapter 1 we restricted the production of each product to be less than or equal to its maximum demand. In the present example we define separate variables for production and sales. Therefore, only the planned sales are to be restricted by the respective demand estimates.

The sales and production of each product must be related via constraints which take the beginning and ending balances of finished products into account. We let the variables y_A and y_B represent the production of the two products. Observing the data presented in Table 2 - 3 we can formulate the following constraints:

$$(2 - 3) \quad 30\ 000 + y_A \geq x_A + 25\ 000,$$
$$18\ 000 + y_B \geq x_B + 28\ 000.$$

The first constraint states that the beginning balance of product A, 30 000 units, plus its production, y_A, must be greater than or equal to the sales, x_A, and the required ending balance, 25 000 units. In the present example it is unnecessary to formulate the constraint in the form of an inequality because the left-hand side will not exceed the right-hand side. However, in the multi-period models of the following chapters this formulation is necessary in order to allow for the possibility of producing for stock in a period to meet the seasonal demand of some later period. The second constraint relates the beginning balance, production, sales, and the ending balance of product B in a respective way.

The constraint relating the capacity required in the production to the available capacity is formulated on the basis of Table 2-2:

$$(2 - 4) \quad 0.5y_A + 0.6y_B \leq 285\ 000.$$

The capacity required is $0.5y_A + 0.6y_B$ and the total available capacity is 285 000 hours.

In the present example we must observe that the beginning balance of each raw material item plus the amount purchased during the period must be greater than or equal to the amount used in the production and the required ending balance:

$$(2 - 5) \quad 45\ 000 + z_w \geq 3y_A + 55\ 000;$$
$$90\ 000 + z_u \geq 2y_B + 80\ 000.$$

The first inequality requires that the beginning balance of raw material W, 45 000 units, plus the purchases for the period, z_w, must equal or exceed the amount used in production, $3y_A$, plus the required ending balance, 55 000 units. The second constraint is interpreted in an analogous manner. The variable z_U represents the planned purchases of raw material U.

We again note that in the present example it is unnecessary to formulate this restriction in the form of an inequality, since we are considering a single period. However, in multi-period models with varying purchase prices of raw materials this formulation is necessary to take into account the possibility of purchasing raw material for seasonal stocks.

The cash constraint requires that the beginning cash balance plus cash receipts from various sources must be greater than or equal to various cash expenditures plus the required minimum ending balance. We again set up the cash constraint in two steps and consider first all fixed cash receipts and expenditures.

The sum of the beginning cash balance and the accounts receivable balance is available for the financing of operations. From this we must deduct the payments for accounts payable, accrued income taxes, amortization of existing loans as well as interest on the outstanding balance, dividends, capital expenditures, and the fixed expenses payable in cash. We get the following constant for the cash constraint:

Available funds			
Beginning cash balance	$ 112 000		
Accounts receivable balance	110 000	$ 222 000	
Less fixed cash expenditures			
Accounts payable, raw materials	$ 38 000		
Accrued income tax	55 000		
Existing loans			
Amortization	$ 10 000		
Interest	5 000	15 000	
Dividends		20 000	
Capital expenditures		250 000	
Fixed costs			
Sales	$ 250 000		
Administration	290 000		
Manufacturing	155 000	695 000	1 073 000
Excess of expenditures over receipts			$ 851 000
Minimum ending cash balance			100 000
Net cash expenditure			$ 951 000

In the present example there are two sources of variable cash receipts, i.e., sales and the proceeds from new loans. The variable cash expenditures are caused by raw material purchases and direct wages and variable overhead of manufacturing. We get the following constraint:

$$(2 - 6) \quad (0.9)(3.5)x_A + (0.95)(4.5)x_B + v \geqq 951\ 000 +$$
$$+ (0.93)(0.15)z_w + (0.85)(0.265)z_U + 1.40y_A + 1.68y_B.$$

We assumed in the preceding section that 90 per cent of the sales revenue of product A is collected in the same period in which the sales take place. The variable x_A represents the number of units sold and the sales price is \$ 3.5/unit. Therefore, the sales revenue of product A is $3.5x_A$ and the cash collections are $(0.9)(3.5)x_A$. Similarly, the cash collections of product B are $(0.95)(4.5)x_B$. The amount of new loans taken is given by the variable v. The fixed cash expenditures including the required ending balance is \$ 951 000. The variable z_W represents the units of raw material W purchased. We assumed that 93 per cent of these purchases must be paid during the same period. It follows that $(0.93)(0.15)z_W$ represents the cash expenditures resulting from the purchases of raw material W. Respectively, $(0.85)(0.265)z_U$ gives the cash expenditures for the purchases of raw material U.

The direct wages and variable manufacturing costs of the products are \$ 1.40 and \$ 1.68, respectively. We assume that all these costs are paid in cash during the same period in which they are incurred. The total amount of cash payments resulting from the production is therefore $1.40y_A + 1.68y_B$.

We assumed in the preceding section that the variable selling costs are 2 per cent of the respective sales prices. However, these costs are not reflected in the cash constraint. This is due to the assumption that the sales commissions representing the variable selling costs are paid one period after the sales. Since we observed them in the objective function, we must consider them as accrued liabilities when we draw up the projected balance sheet. If they had been paid during the planning period we would have observed them by adding the terms $(0.02)(3.5)x_A +$ $+ (0.02)(4.5)x_B$ to the right-hand side of the cash constraint given in (2 - 6). We also have to observe that the interest expense on new loans is not among the cash expenditures. The implication is that the interest is payable one period after the loan is taken. On the other, the fixed cash expenditures include the \$ 5 000 interest on the existing loans.

We now assume that the firm can improve its cash position by taking new loans if this is desirable. However, the creditors have stipulated that a limit of \$ 50 000 must be observed.

This is taken into account by the following constraint:

(2 - 7) $v \leq 50\ 000$.

Finally we need a constraint to compute the interest expenses which were deducted from the contribution in the objective function:

(2 - 8) $r = 0.1v + 5\ 000$.

This equation implies that new loans require the payment of interest of 10 per cent per period. We have formulated the constraint in a way such that the variable r represents the sum of the interest of both new and existing loans. The value of the variable r can now be used in the formulation of the projected income statement. However, for the purposes of obtaining the optimal solution to the problem it is unnecessary to have the fixed interest expense of \$ 5 000 in the equation. It follows that \$ 5 000 fixed expenses have been included solely for convenience.

All variables must be nonnegative. Nonnegativity constraints (2 - 9) take care of this requirement:

$$(2 - 9) \quad x_A, \; x_B, \; y_A, \; y_B, \; z_W, \; z_U, \; v, \; r \geq 0.$$

Our problem is to maximize (2 - 1) subject to the constraints (2 - 2) to (2 - 9).

Preparation of Data Input

The problem will be solved utilizing the computer program presented in Appendix B. In this program it is not necessary to have all the constraints in the form in which the right-hand side constants are either positive or zeros, as is required in the manual Simplex-procedure. However, in this example we will arrange th constraints in the form required by the Simplex procedure by multiplying the constraints by (-1) whenever necessary to convert the negative right-hand side constants into positive constants. In this multiplication we must of course observe that the direction of the inequality sign must simultaneously be reversed. Rearranging the constraints we get the following model:

Maximize $Z = 1.58x_A + 2.20x_B \qquad\qquad -r$

Subject to

$$
\begin{array}{llll}
x_A & & & \leq 250\ 000 \\
& x_B & & \leq 300\ 000 \\
x_A & -y_A & & \leq 5\ 000 \\
-x_B & +y_B & & \geq 10\ 000 \\
0.5y_A & + 0.6y_B & & \leq 285\ 000 \\
-3y_A & & +z_W & \geq 10\ 000 \\
2y_B & & -z_U & \leq 10\ 000
\end{array}
$$

49

$$3.15x_A + 4.28x_B - 1.4y_A - 1.68y_B - 0.14z_W - 0.22z_U + v \quad = 951\,000$$
$$v \quad = 50\,000$$
$$-0.1v + r \quad = \quad 5\,000$$

and

$$x_A,\ x_B,\ y_A,\ y_B,\ z_W,\ z_U,\ v,\ r \geqq 0.$$

The input to the computer program is given in the form of punch-cards. For the preparation of the data cards and the interpretation of the computer output we rearrange the above model in the form of a table where the columns represent the variables as well as the right-hand side vector of the model. The rows represent the objective and the constraints, excluding the nonnegativity constraints. Table 2 - 8 presents the model in the required form. The names given to the columns are the variables of the model plus the name "STIPUL" given to the right-hand side column. The names of the rows are also self-explanatory. The objective function is designated by "CONTRIB", the upper limit of the sales of product A by "SALEA", etc. The program requires that a card is punched for each nonzero element of the resulting matrix, as explained in the Appendix.

	XA	XB	YA	YB	ZW	ZU	V	R	STIPUL
CONTRIB	1.58	2.20						-1.	
SALEA	1.								250 000.
SALEB		1.							300 000.
INVENA	1.		-1.						5 000.
INVENB		-1		1.					10 000.
PRODCA			0.5	0.6					285 000.
RAWMAW			-3.		1.				10 000.
RAWMAU			2.			-1.			10 000.
CASH	3.15	4.28	-1.40	-1.68	-0.14	-0.22	1.		951 000.
LOAN							1.		50 000.
INTEREST							-0.1	1.	5 000.

Table 2-8. The model arranged for the keypunching of the input cards.

Analysis of Computer Output

The computer output is presented in Table 2-9. The problem has 10 constraints in addition to the nonnegativity constraints. In the preceding chapter we noted that the solution of a linear programming problem contains as many variables as there are such constraints. It follows that we must find 10 variables which form the optimal program. Some of these variables may be slack variables which were added to the model by the computer. The program that we have used indicates the variables in the program by printing the sign B* in the VARIABLE TYPE-column. The same sign indicates the objective function. Checking Table 2 - 9 we can find 11 lines with the sign B*

In most cases we find the sign Bx on a line which represents sales, production, raw material purchases, or some other variable of the model. However, the line with the title "SALEA" is an exception. SALEA was a name given to a constraint. In this case we must interpret the results by observing that the program added a slack variable to this constraint and that the slack variable is now in the optimal program. The value of the slack variable is the difference between the following figures:

	SOLUTION ACTIVITY	UPPER BOUND
SALEA B*	203 000.000	250 000.000

Unutilized sales possibilities are the difference between the upper bound on demand, 250 000 units, and the actual planned sales, 203 000 units, or 47 000 units.

The upper limit of new loans does not effectively bind the optimal solution. Consequently, the slack variable associated with this constraint is also at a positive level. By deducting the figure in the SOLUTION ACTIVITY-column on the LOAN-row from the figure in the UPPER BOUND-column on the same row we can see that

50 000 - 44 310 = $ 5 690

unutilized credit lines exist in the optimal solution. We can now list the optimal program:

VARIABLE	ENTRIES TYPE		SOLUTION ACTIVITY	UPPER BOUND	LOWER BOUND	CURRENT COST	REDUCED COST
XA	B*	4	203000.000	**********	0.000	1.579	0.000
CONTRIB	B*	0	971309.000	**********	**********	-1.000	-1.000
XB	B*	4	300000.000	**********	0.000	2.200	0.000
SALEA	B*	0	203000.000	250000.000	0.000	0.000	0.000
SALEB	UL	0	300000.000	300000.000	0.000	0.000	-0.360
INVENA	UL	0	5000.000	5000.000	0.000	0.000	-1.895
YA	B*	4	198000.000	**********	0.000	0.000	0.000
INVENB	LL	0	10000.000	**********	10000.000	0.000	-2.267
YB	B*	4	309999.999	**********	0.000	0.000	0.000
PRODCA	UL	0	285000.000	285000.000	0.000	0.000	-3.426
RAWMAW	LL	0	10000.000	**********	10000.000	0.000	-0.014
ZW	B*	2	603999.999	**********	0.000	0.000	0.000
RAWMAU	UL	0	10000.000	10000.000	0.000	0.000	-0.021
ZU	B*	2	609999.999	**********	0.000	0.000	0.000
CASH	LL	0	951000.000	**********	951000.000	0.000	-0.100
V	B*	3	44309.997	**********	0.000	0.000	0.000
R	B*	2	9430.999	**********	0.000	-1.000	0.000
LOAN	B*	0	44309.997	50000.000	0.000	0.000	0.000
INTERESTEQ	Q	0	5000.000	5000.000	5000.000	0.000	-1.000

Table 2-9. Solution to the Single-Period Model.

52

Products

Sales

$x_A = 203\,000$ units
$x_B = 300\,000$ »

Production

$y_A = 198\,000$ units
$y_B = 310\,000$ »

Raw Materials

$z_W = 604\,000$ units
$z_U = 610\,000$ »

New Loans

$v = \$\,44\,310$

Interest

$r = \$\,9\,431$

Generation of Budgets

Taking the computer output, the model, and the underlying data we can now formulate the budgets for the various functions of the firm as well as the projected financial statements. All these budgets will now be compatible with each other because we derive them from a simultaneous solution.

In the present example as well as in the remaining examples of the present text we assume that we derive the budgets manually after the computer solution has been obtained. This does not mean, however, that in actual applications we would have to go through the same procedure. We can take the computer output in some other form, e.g., punched cards, and utilize additional computer programs to generate the budgets directly from the computer output without manual intervention. However, these programs must be developed for each particular application, since they do not exist in commercially sold packages.

Sales, Production and Purchase Budgets

The sales budget can be developed by taking the values of x_A and x_B in the optimal program:

	Total $	Price	Product A Units	$	Price	Product B Units	$
Sales	2 060 500	3.50	203 000	710 500	5.5	300 000	1 350 000
./. Selling Costs	41 210	0.07		14 210	0.09		27 000
Net Sales	2 019 290			696 290			1 323 000
./. Std.–Costs of Sales	1 038 550	1.85		375 550	2.21		663 000
Contribution Margin	980 740			320 740			660 000

Table 2-10. The Sales Budget.

The production and inventory budget can be derived by taking Table 2 - 3 and the optimal values of the variables x_A, x_B, y_A, and y_B:

	Product A	Product B
Desired Ending Inventory	25 000	28 000
Plus: Sales	x_A = 203 000	x_B = 300 000
Total Requirements	228 000	328 000
Less: Beginning Inventory	30 000	18 000
Required Production	y_A = 198 000	y_B = 310 000

Table 2-11. Production and Inventory Budget.

In multi-period models the ending inventory of some periods may exceed the required minimum if it is advisable to produce for stock in order to meet seasonal demand fluctuations. In a single period model the ending inventory will always be at the desired minimum level because the model is not able to look beyond the end of the first period.

We assumed in the model that the work in process inventories remain at the level of the beginning balance sheet. This enables us to develop the budget for raw material purchases on the basis of the production variables, y_A and y_B, and the variables for raw material purchases, z_W and z_U:

	Raw Materials W	U
Desired Ending Inventory	55 000	80 000
Plus: Production Requirements	$3y_A$ = 594 000	$2y_B$ = 620 000
Total Requirements	649 000	700 000
Less: Beginning Balance	45 000	90 000
Required Purchases	z_W = 604 000	z_U = 610 000

Table 2-12. Budgeted Raw Material Purchases.

Both production and purchasing budgets can be converted into dollar figures by multiplying the physical units by their standard costs.

Cash Budget

Cash budget can be constructed with the help of terms that appear in the constraint (2 - 6). The model was formulated in such a way that the firm does not have any possibility to invest its excess funds outside the firm in case the cash generated by the sales exceeds the cash required for the operations and the fixed cash expenditures. Therefore, we must first check whether there are excessive funds in the ending cash balance. By checking the figure in the SOLUTION ACTIVITY-column on the CASH-row we note that it is equal to the figure in the LOWER BOUND-column on the same row, 951 000. The difference between these two figures gives the value of the slack variable associated with the cash constraint. In this example the value of the variable is zero. We therefore know that the ending balance of cash is the required minimum amount of $ 100 000. This conclusion can also be drawn on the basis of the fact that new loans are included in the optimal solution. Since the loan taken during the period involves interest expenses which reduce the value of the objective function, the solution will include new loans only to the minimum possible amount.

Excessive cash would appear in the model only in the case where no new loans are needed. The value of the slack variable would then indicate the amount of excess cash and the total amount of ending balance would be the minimum required amount ($ 100 000) plus the value of the slack variable. The formulation of the model (2-1) to (2-9) is not perfect because we did not define a variable for the excess cash. It would be better to define an explicit variable and include it in the cash constraint as well as in the objective function. If the firm can invest excess funds profitably outside the firm, then the coefficient of this variable in the objective function would indicate the return on this investment. This way we would avoid the possibility existing in the present formulation according to which the model may in certain cases invest excess cash, e.g., in raw material. This possibility arises only when the operations generate excess funds to such an extent that the firm needs no new additional loans. Since the present example involves the taking of new loans, we do not have to worry about this malfunctioning of the model.

We set up the cash budget starting from the beginning cash balance, adding to it the various cash receipts and deducting from it the various cash expenditures:

Beginning Cash					$ 112 000
Cash receipts					
Fixed					
Accounts receivable balance			110 000		
Variable					
Sales					
A: $(0.9)(3.5)x_A = (3.15)203\,000$	$= 639\,450$				
B: $(0.95)(4.5)x_B = (4.28)300\,000$	$= \underline{1\,284\,000}$	1 923 450			
New loans			44 310		2 077 760
Funds available					$ 2 189 760
Cash expenditures					
Fixed					
Accounts payable			93 000		
Existing loans					
Amortization	10 000				
Interest	5 000		15 000		
Dividends			20 000		
Investment budget			250 000		
Fixed expenses			695 000	1 073 000	
Variable					
Production					
A: $(1.4)y_A = (1.4)198\,000$	277 200				
B: $(1.68)y_B = (1.68)31\,000$	520 800			798 000	
Purchases					
W: $(0.93)(0.15)z_W = (0.14)604\,000$	84 560				
U: $(0.85)(0.265)z_U = (0.22)610\,000$	134 200			218 760	2 089 760
Ending Cash Balance					$ 100 000

Table 2-13. Cash Budget.

Projected Income Statement

The projected income statement can be drawn up by beginning with the contribution of the sales budget and deducting from it interest expenses and the fixed cost budgets. The fixed costs are given in Table 2-7. The optimal value of the variable R in Table 2-9 gives the total interest expenses for both the existing and new loans.

The optimal value of the objective function can be read from Table 2-9, where it is given in the SOLUTION ACTIVITY-column on the CONTRIB-row. It is the difference between the total contribution and the interest expenses.

The projected income statement is computed assuming that the federal income tax rate is 50 per cent and that the taxes accrued in this period are paid in the next period. It follows that we must include the

Sales		$ 2 060 500
Less: Variable Selling Costs		41 210
Net Sales		2 019 290
Less: Standard Cost of Sales		1 038 550
Contribution		980 740
Less: Interest Expenses		9 431
The Value of Objective Function		971 309
Less: Fixed Costs		
Sales	310 000	
Administration	340 000	
Manufacturing	265 000	915 000
Profit before Tax		56 309
Less: Income Tax (50 %)		28 154.50
Net Operating Profit		28 154.50

Table 2-14. Projected Income Statement.

accrued income taxes in the liabilities of the projected balance sheet.

Projected Balance Sheet

The beginning balance sheet, optimal solution, and the projected income statement are utilized to develop the projected balance sheet which is given in Table 2-15. The ending cash balance of the cash budget also gives the cash balance of the balance sheet. The accounts receivable balance has been developed by taking the value of the variables x_A and x_B and multiplying these by the fraction of the sales prices that remain uncollected at the end of the period.

The raw material ending balances are developed by multiplying the unit ending balances of Table 2-12 by their respective standard costs. The ending balance of work in process is the same as the beginning balance, since no change was assumed during the period. The ending balance of finished products is the physical inventory of Table 2-11 multiplied by the respective standard manufacturing costs.

Prepaid expenses are at the level of the beginning balance. Fixed assets are increased by new acquisitions, $ 250 000, and decreased by depreciation.

Accounts payable balances are developed by multiplying the raw material purchases by the fraction of the purchase price which is not paid during the period. Accrued salaries and wages are assumed to remain at the level of the beginning balance. Accrued interest is due to the new loans. It is the value of the variable "R" in the optimal solution less $ 5 000 which refers to the interest payments included in the fixed cash expenditures. The accrued selling costs are stated in the sales budget. The accrued income tax was calculated in the projected income statement. Other accounts payable are assumed to remain at their previous level.

57

Existing loans of the ending balance are the difference between the beginning balance and repayments plus the new loans taken during the period. The value of the variable v is $ 44 310 in the optimal program.

Equity is decreased by the dividends, $ 20 000, paid during the period and increased by the net operating profit of the year, $ 28 150.50.

Assets

Current Assets				
Cash			100 000	
Accounts Receivable				
A: (3.5–3.15) 203 000		71 050		
B: (4.5–4.28) 300 000		66 000	137 050	
Inventories				
Raw Materials				
W: (0.15) 55 000		8 250		
U: (0.265) 80 000		21 200	29 450	
Work in Process			87 900	
Finished Products				
A: (1.85) 25 000		46 250		
B: (2.21) 28 000		61 880	108 130	462 530
Prepaid Expenses				6 200
Fixed Assets				
Beginning Balance		1 058 220		
Acquisitions		250 000	1 308 220	
Depreciation			220 000	1 088 220
				$ 1 556 950

Liabilities

Accounts Payable				
Raw materials				
W: (0.15–0.14) 604 000		6 040		
U: (0.264–0.22) 610 000		27 450	33 490	
Accrued Wages			78 000	
Accrued Interest			4 431	
Accrued Commissions			41 210	
Accrued Income Tax			28 154.50	
Other Accounts Payable			37 500	222 786.50
Long-Term Debt				
Beginning Balance		100 000		
Repayments		10 000	90 000	
New Loans			44 310	134 310
Equity				
Shareholders' Capital			900 000	
Undistributed Profit	291 700			
Dividends	20 000	271 700		
Profit for the Period		28 150.50	299 854.50	1 199 854.50
				$ 1 556 950

Table 2–15. Projected Balance Sheet.

Analysis of the Shadow Prices

The sales possibilities of product A cannot be exhausted. This was indicated by the value of the respective slack variable associated with the upper limit of sales of product A which takes the value of 47 000 units. The contribution could be increased if the firm had more units of product A available. The required ending balances of finished products were given in Table 2-3. We can now use the shadow prices associated with constraints (2-3) to evaluate the effect of a reduction in these requirements. Let us consider first the effect of reducing the required ending inventory of product A by one unit from 25 000 to 24 999 units.

A superficial analysis might result in an answer: the objective will be increased by the unit contribution of product A, $ 1.58. However, the shadow price associated with the inventory constraint of product A, which can be found in the REDUCED COST-column on the INVENA-row of Table 2-9, indicates that the objective would be incereased by $ 1.895 for each unit reduction.

Since the shadow price shows the net effect of all changes induced by an optimal response to a one unit change in the right-hand side constant, it shows in addition to the increase in contribution also the result of increased funds made available by the sale. According to Table 2-8 the coefficient associated with the variable x_A in the cash constraint is $ 3.15 per unit. For each additional unit of product A sold out of the ending inventory the available cash is increased by $ 3.15. New loans are reduced by the same amount and, therefore, the interest expenses are reduced by $(0.1)3.15 = $ 0.315$. The total net effect is $ 1.58 + + $ 0.315 = $ 1.895 per unit which is also the value of the shadow price.

The sales possibilities of product B are used up. Still, a reduction of one unit in the ending inventory of product B increases the objective by $ 2.267. A one unit reduction in the ending inventory reduces the capacity requirements by 0.6 hours. This capacity is available for the production of product A. It follows that we can increase the production and sales of A by $(0.6)/(0.5) = 1.2$ units. The net change in financing requirements is

$$(1.2) \ [3.15 - 1.40 - 3(0.14)] \ + 1.68 + 2(0.22) = $ 3.716$$

net cash income. The change in financing costs is a 10 per cent interest saving on this, i.e., $ 0.371. The increase in contribution is $ 1.58 per unit on 1.2 units, or $ 1.896. The shadow price is the sum of these, $ 2.267.

In more complicated models it can be very difficult to trace out all changes resulting from a one unit change in some right-hand side constant. The great advantage of shadow prices is that they give us this information as a byproduct of the optimal solution. This information can sometimes produce surprising results. Even in this small example it is somewhat surprising that the greatest increase in the objective comes from the reduction of the ending inventory of product B for which there are no additional sales possibilities available. This shows the advantage of the use of a formal optimization model over informal methods. The model is solved in a way which does not "forget" to consider alternatives which would not be brought under analysis in an intuitive solution.

The shadow price associated with the right-hand side constant of the capacity constraint shows that an additional hour of production capacity made available to the firm without charge would produce an increase of $ 3.426 in the objective. An additional capacity hour would obviously be used for the making of product A. The resulting increase in the objective is different from the contribution of two additional units of A that can be made by one capacity hour. Again, the resulting changes in the cash position are reflected in the shadow price.

The shadow price associated with the cash constraint is $ 0.1/$. If the right-hand side constant were reduced by one dollar, for example, by reducing the required minimum ending cash balance from $ 100 000 to $ 99 999, the objective would be increased by $ 0.1. The change in the objective is therefore equal to the interest rate on new loans. The reduction in the right-hand side constant would reduce the loan requirements by one dollar. This would again reduce interest expenses by $ 0.1. This shadow price is valid only to the point where the upper limit on new loans becomes effectively binding. After this point the interest rate no longer reflects the value of an additional dollar.

The shadow prices associated with raw material constraints can be directly derived from the interest rate on new loans. If the minimum ending balances of raw materials were reduced, the objective would increase by the amount of interest on the funds tied up by a raw material unit.

Finally, it is worth noting that the shadow price associated with the upper limit of the sales of product B is $ 0.36. This may appear to be a surprising result. The unit contribution of product B in itself is $ 2.20 and we should consider the additional effects of changes in the cash position. The shadow price shows again the net change in the objective after all adjustements, however. The increase in the sales of product B will induce an increase in its production, and this will again reduce the production and sales of product A by 1.2 units, since there is a shortage of production capacity.

A Single-Period Multi-Plant Model

Model Formulation

Modern firms usually have several plants and sales districts. The models of these firms must observe the existing possibility to transport products from plant to plant. In order to demonstrate the resulting model structure we next generalize the model presented in Table 2-8 to cover two plants and two marketing districts. The inclusion of several plants and/or sales districts would not bring in any basically new features and in order to keep the size of the example as small as possible we limit our analysis to the smallest possible multiplant firm.

We assume that the data presented in Tables 2-1 to 2-7 are still valid. The single plant of the preceding section is assumed to be the parent plant which centrally manages the financing of the operations of both plants. The subscript P will identify the parent plant variables. The variables needing identification as to the plant are sales, production, and raw material purchases. For example, z_{UP} denotes the purchases of raw material U for plant P. Respectively, the subscript S identifies the subsidiary plant. The variable z_{US} denotes the purchases of raw material U for plant S.

The beginning balance presented in Table 2-6 remains valid except for the beginning inventories in the subsidiary plant. We assume that these balances are the following:

Raw Materials		
W: (0.15) 20 000	= $ 3 000	
U: (0.265) 30 000	= $ 7 950	10 950
Work in Process		9 100
Finished Products		
A: (2.13) 20 000	= $ 42 600	
B: (2.49) 15 000	= $ 37 350	79 950
		$ 100 000

Table 2-16. The beginning inventories of the subsidiary plant.

The beginning balance of the whole corporation could now be presented by including beginning balances of Table 2-16 in the assets and $ 100 000 in the equity of the balance sheet presented in Table 2-6. We assume, in other words, that the dollar figure for fixed assets in Table 2-6 now covers the book value of fixed assets in both plants. A further assumption is that the management attempts to reduce both raw material and finished

61

product inventories in the subsidiary plant by 10 per cent for all items.

Table 2-16 indicates that the cost structure of the subsidiary plant is somewhat different from that of the parent plant. This structure is presented in detail in Table 2-17. The production in the subsidiary plant is for some reason less efficient than in the main plant. This is evident by looking at the standard production hours of both products in Table 2-17. The standard labor rates, on the other hand, are somewhat lower than in the main plant. The standard rate for variable overhead is 20 per cent higher than in the parent plant. The standard raw material costs are equal in both plants. We assume that 200 000 hours of production capacity are available in the planning period.

Cost element	Product A	Product B
Raw materials		
3 units of raw material W à $ 0.15/unit	0.45	–
2 units of raw material U à $ 0.265/unit	–	0.53
Direct Wages		
0.6 hours à $ 1.60 per hour	0.96	–
0.7 hours à $ 1.60 per hour	–	1.12
Variable Overhead $ 1.20 per hour	0.72	0.84
Total Variable Costs	2.13	2.49

Table 2–17. The cost structure of the products made in the subsidiary plant.

Table 2-18 presents the upper limits of demand for both products as well as their selling prices in the marketing area of the subsidiary plant. We assume that the subsidiary plant is able to sell at somewhat higher prices than the parent plant. The demand for both products is much lower in the sales area of the subsidiary plant, however.

Product	Price $/unit	Sales Possibilites units
A	3.80	180 000
B	4.60	150 000

Table 2–18. The demand for products in the subsidiary plant.

The fixed cost budget must be developed for the subsidiary plant like it was presented for the parent plant. This budget is given in Table 2-19. We assume that the depreciation included in this budget is in addition to the total depreciation given in Table 2-7, although a common fixed assets figure was assumed for both plants in the beginning balance.

Finally we need data on the cost of transporting finished products from one factory to the other. We assume that the cost of transportation of one unit of a product from plant P to S costs the same as the transportation of the same product in the opposite direction (which need not be

```
Fixed Costs
Selling
    Depreciation                         10 000
    Cash Expenditure                    200 000
                                     $ 210 000

Administration
    Depreciation                         10 000
    Cash Expenditure                     90 000
                                     $ 100 000

Manufacturing
    Depreciation                         30 000
    Cash Expenditure                    210 000
                                     $ 240 000
```

Table 2-19. The fixed cost budget for the subsidiary plant.

the case in real applications). The cost of transporting is \$ 0.30 per unit for product A and \$ 0.40 per unit for product B. All these costs are paid in cash.

Since the cost structure of the final products is different in different plants we must assume something about the treatment of cost differences. In order to avoid considerations about whether to use FIFO-, LIFO-, or moving average costing, etc., we reflect the cost difference in the objective function at the moment the product is transported between the plants. This simplifies the use of variables and the costing of ending inventories. In other words, both plants transfer the products at their own standard costs and receive the products valued at their own standard costs. The cost difference either increases or decreases the objective depending on the direction of the transportation.

We use the variable t to represent the units of product transported between the plants. The subscripts are used in the following way:

t_{APS} = units of product A transported to parent from subsidiary,

t_{BPS} = units of product B transported to parent from subsidiary,

t_{ASP} = units of product A transported to subsidiary from parent,

t_{BSP} = units of product B transported to subsidiary from parent.

Using the preceding data we can now formulate a common model for both plants. We again begin by the objective function:

$$\text{Maximize } Z = (3.50 - 0.07 - 1.85)x_{AP} + (4.5 - 0.09 - 2.21)x_{BP}$$

$$(2\text{-}10) \quad + (1.85 - 2.13 - 0.30)t_{APS} + (2.21 - 2.49 - 0.40)t_{BPS}$$

$$+ (2.13 - 1.85 - 0.30)t_{ASP} + (2.49 - 2.21 - 0.40)t_{BSP}$$

$$+ (3.80 - 0.07 - 2.13)x_{AS} + (.460 - 0.09 - 2.49)x_{BS} - r.$$

63

The coefficients of the variables in the objective function have been developed for the variables representing the units of product sold by beginning with the selling price applicable for the sales district and deducting from it the variable selling and manufacturing costs. For simplicity we assume that the variable selling costs are the same in both sales districts. The variables representing the products transprted between the plants are multiplied by coefficients which have been developed by taking the difference in standard manufacturing costs in the plants and by deducting from this difference the cost of transportation between the plants.

The first set of constraints sets an upper limit to the sales of each product in each marketing area:

$$(2\text{-}11) \quad \begin{aligned} x_{AP} &\le 250\ 000, \\ x_{BP} &\le 300\ 000, \\ x_{AS} &\le 180\ 000, \\ x_{BS} &\le 150\ 000. \end{aligned}$$

The first two inequalities represent the upper limits of demand of the parent plant. The remaining two inequalities are related to the subsidiary plant.

The constraints that relate the beginning balances and the production of finished products to the sales and the ending balances are slightly different from inequalities (2-3) because we now assume that it is possible to transport products between the plants:

$$(2\text{-}12) \quad \begin{aligned} 30\ 000 + y_{AP} + t_{APS} &\ge x_{AP} + t_{ASP} + 25\ 000, \\ 18\ 000 + y_{BP} + t_{BPS} &\ge x_{BP} + t_{BSP} + 28\ 000, \\ 20\ 000 + y_{AS} + t_{ASP} &\ge x_{AS} + t_{APS} + 18\ 000, \\ 15\ 000 + y_{BS} + t_{BSP} &\ge x_{BS} + t_{BPS} + 13\ 500. \end{aligned}$$

The amount of a product transported to a plant must now be added to the number of units available. On the other hand, the units transported from a plant must be deducted from the units available, or, which is the same thing, added to the sum of sales and ending balances.

There is now a separate constraint for each plant relating the capacity used to the available capacity:

$$(2\text{-}13) \quad \begin{aligned} 0.5 y_{AP} + 0.6 y_{BP} &\le 285\ 000, \\ 0.6 y_{AS} + 0.7 y_{BS} &\le 200\ 000. \end{aligned}$$

The raw material constraints have the same structure as those of the preceding model:

$$
\begin{aligned}
45\ 000 + z_{WP} &\geq 3y_{AP} + 55\ 000, \\
90\ 000 + z_{UP} &\geq 2y_{BP} + 80\ 000, \\
20\ 000 + z_{WS} &\geq 3y_{AS} + 18\ 000, \\
30\ 000 + z_{US} &\geq 2y_{BS} + 27\ 000.
\end{aligned}
$$

(2-14)

Both fixed and variable cash payments are effected by the inclusion of the subsidiary plant. The net fixed cash expenditures which were \$ 951 000 in constraint (2-6) must now be increased by the fixed cash expenditures of the subsidiary plant, \$ 500 000. The constant on the right-hand side of the cash constraint is now the sum of these two amounts, \$ 1 451 000. In addition to the sales and production of the subsidiary plant we must also include the cash expenditures resulting from the transportation of products between the plants. We assume that all transportation costs are paid in cash:

(2-15)
$$
\begin{aligned}
& 3.15x_{AP} + 4.28x_{BP} + (0.9)3.8x_{AS} + (0.95)4.6x_{BS} + v \geq \\
& 1\ 451\ 000 + 0.14z_{WP} + 0.14z_{WS} + 0.22z_{UP} + 0.22z_{US} + 1.4y_{AP} \\
& + 1.68y_{BP} + 1.68y_{AS} + 1.96y_{BS} + 0.3t_{APS} + 0.3t_{ASP} + \\
& 0.4t_{BPS} + 0.4t_{BSP}.
\end{aligned}
$$

The terms of payment for the sales of the subsidiary plant are assumed to be the same as those of the parent. The direct wages and variable overhead are paid in cash and the raw material purchased on the same terms in both plants.

The upper limit of new loans remains the same as before:

(2-16) $V \leq 50\ 000.$

The total interest expenses are also computed by the same equation as in the preceding model:

(2-17) $r = 5\ 000 + 0.1v.$

As in every linear programming problem, we must require that all variables are nonnegative.

Solution

The objective function and the constraints of the twoplant problem are exhibited in Table 2-20. The upper left-hand corner represents the constraints of the parent plant. The lower right-hand side corner again shows the constraints of the subsidiary plant. These two blocks are connected by the transportation matrix shown in the middle of the table. All nonzero elements of this matrix are either (+1) or (-1). The coefficient (-1) indicates the plant which sends the product and the coefficient (+1) indicates the plant which receives it. In other words, the constraints (2-11) to (2-14) have been arranged so that the variables referring to the parent plant are in the left-hand side, the variables referring to the transportation of the products in the middle, and the variables referring to the subsidiary plant in the right-hand side of the table.

The three blocks of the table are connected byt the objective function which has been presented at the top of the table. It now has nonzero elements in all three blocks. The cash constraint also ties the different blocks together. This constraint is presented at the bottom of the table. The two variables next to the inequality signs represent the taking of new loans and the interest charges. Some of the right-hand side constraints are now negative because the program utilized for solving the example does not require that constraints should first be arranged to be either positive or zero.

The construction of multi-plant models in blocks like those exhibited in Table 2-20 facilitates the work on large-scale models. Nonzero elements can be located in the matrix with the help of special programs.

The model can also be utilized for the generation of single plant programs. This can be achieved by the elimination of the transportation variables. Library programs of most computer manufacturers contain features for the elimination of some rows and/or columns of the matrix. We could, for example, first solve the problem without the columns TAPS, TASP, TBPS, and TBSP. This would imply that both plants are operating separately. After the solution, we could add these columns to the model and develop an integrated plan for the whole firm.

The solution to this problem is given in Tables 2-21a and 2-21b. In this solution we consider the possibility of transporting products between the plants. In this example, the demand, price and cost structure is such that the transportation of products between the plants is not profitable. Variables x_{AP} and x_{BP} represent the sales of the products in the parent plant. Variables y_{AP} and y_{BP} give the production in the parent plant. The optimal values of all these variables are the same as those in the single-plant model. The optimal values of the transportation variables are all zeros. The sales in the

	XAP	XBP	YAP	YBP	ZWP	ZUP	TAPS	TASP	TBPS	TBSP	XAS	XBS	YAS	YBS	ZWS	ZUS	V	R	STIP
CONTR	1.58	2.20					-0.58	-0.02	-0.68	-0.12	1.60	2.02						-1	
PSALEA	1.						1.	-1.											≤ 250 000
PSALEB		1.							1.	-1.									≤ 300 000
PINVENA	-1.		1.																≥ -5 000
PINVENB		-1.		1.															≤ 10 000
PPRODCA			0.5	0.6															≤ 285 000
PRAWMAW			-3.		1.														≤ 10 000
PRAWMAU				-2.		1.													≥ -10 000
SSALEA							-1.	1.			1.								≤ 180 000
SSALEB									-1.	1.		1.							≤ 150 000
SINVENA											-1.		1.						≥ -2 000
SINVENB												-1.		1.					≥ -1 500
SPRODCA													0.6	0.7					≤ 200 000
SRAWMAW													-3		1.				≥ -2 000
SRAWMAU														-2.		1.			≥ -3 000
CASH	3.15	4.28	-1.4	-1.68	-0.14	-0.22	-0.3	-0.3	-0.4	-0.4	3.42	4.37	-1.68	-1.96	-0.14	-0.22	1.		≤ 1 451 000
DEBTLIM																	1.		≤ 50 000
INTEREST																	-0.1	1.	= 5 000

Table 2-20. Two-Plant Model Structure.

subsidiary plant show the same tendency as the sales in the parent plant. The production capacity is first allocated to product B until its demand is saturated. The remaining capacity is then allocated to product A.

The figures in the REDUCED COST-column on the rows representing the transportation on finished products indicate the reduction in the objective function resulting from the transportation of one unit of product. For example, the figure on the TASP-row is almost zero. If the transportation cost of product A to the subsidiary from the parent plant were $ 0.2 per unit instead of $ 0.3 assumed in the example, it would pay to transport product A from parent to subsidiary even though it is not possible to satisfy the demand for this product in the parent plant.

However, it is not necessary to have changes in the cost structure in order to induce transportation in the present model. The only change made to the present model in problem 2-2 is an increase in the production capacity of the subsidiary plant. The optimal solution now includes the transportation of product B between the plants.

Development of Budgets

The generation of budgets on the basis of the optimal solution exhibited in Tables 2-21a and 2-21b follows the approach presented in connection with the single-plant model. This time we will exhibit only the projected financial statements. These have been presented in tables 2-22 and 2-23.

The order of the representation of the various items in the income statement is slightly different from that normally presented in accounting textbooks. We deduct from the total contribution of the plants the joint interest expenses, and only after that we deduct the fixed costs of the plants. In traditional accounting we would first compute the profit of each plant after the deduction of its fixed costs and from the sum of the plant profits we would then deduct the joint interest expenses. The reason for the order of computation in Table 2-22 is that we want to check the profit after interest with the value of the objective function in Table 2-21a. In the present example the optimal value of the objective function is the total contribution less interest charges, since we don't have any transportation of products.

The projected balance sheet has been drawn up to separately show the current assets of the two plants. If the beginning balance had listed the fixed assets by the plant we could complete the projected income statement by computing the return on investment in each plant.

The plantwise sales, production, and purchasing budgets could be drawn up in the way exhibited in Tables 2-10, 2-11, and 2-12. If the

VARIABLE	TYPE	ENTRIES	SOLUTION ACTIVITY	UPPER BOUND	LOWER BOUND	CURRENT COST	REDUCED COST
XAP	B*	4	203000.000	**********	0.000	1.579	0.000
CONTRIB	B*	0	1535461.333	**********	**********	-1.000	-1.000
XBP	B*	4	300000.000	**********	0.000	2.200	0.000
TAPS	LL	4	0.000	**********	0.000	-0.579	-0.656
TASP	LL	4	0.000	**********	0.000	-0.020	-0.003
TBPS	LL	4	0.000	**********	0.000	-0.679	-0.713
TBSP	LL	4	0.000	**********	0.000	-0.120	-0.166
XAS	B*	4	162083.334	**********	0.000	1.600	0.000
XBS	B*	4	150000.000	**********	0.000	2.020	0.000
R	B*	2	7611.999	**********	0.000	-1.000	0.000
PSALEA	B*	0	203000.000	250000.000	0.000	0.000	0.000
PINVENA	LL	0	-5000.000	**********	-5000.000	0.000	-1.895
PSALEB	UL	0	300000.000	300000.000	0.000	0.000	-0.360
PINVENB	LL	0	10000.000	**********	10000.000	0.000	-2.267
YAP	B*	4	198000.000	**********	0.000	0.000	0.000
PPRODCA	UL	0	285000.000	285000.000	0.000	0.000	-3.426
PRAWMAW	LL	0	10000.000	**********	10000.000	0.000	-0.014
YBP	B*	4	310000.000	**********	0.000	0.000	0.000

Table 2-21a. Solution to the Two-Plant Model.

PRAWMAU	LL	0	-10000.000	************	-10000.000	0.000	-0.021
ZWP	B*	2	603999.999	************	0.000	0.000	0.000
ZUP	B*	2	610000.000	************	0.000	0.000	-0.000
SINVENA	LL	0	-2000.000	************	-2000.000	0.000	-1.942
SINVENB	LL	0	-1500.000	************	-1500.000	0.000	-2.260
SSALEA	B*	0	162083.334	180000.000	0.000	0.000	0.000
SSALEB	UL	0	150000.000	150000.000	0.000	0.000	-0.196
YAS	B*	4	160083.334	************	0.000	0.000	0.000
SPRODCA	UL	0	200000.000	200000.000	0.000	0.000	-2.886
SRAWMAW	LL	0	-2000.000	************	-2000.000	0.000	-0.014
YBS	B*	4	148500.000	************	0.000	0.000	0.000
SRAWMAU	LL	0	-3000.000	************	-3000.000	0.000	-0.022
ZWS	B*	2	478250.001	************	0.000	0.000	0.000
ZUS	B*	2	294000.000	************	0.000	0.000	0.000
CASH	LL	0	1451000.001	************	1451000.001	0.000	-0.100
V	B*	3	26119.998	************	0.000	0.000	0.000
DEBTLIM	B*	0	26119.998	50000.000	0.000	0.000	0.000
INTERESTEQ		0	5000.000	5000.000	5000.000	0.000	-1.000

Table 2-21b. Solution to the Two-Plant Model.

70

Projected income statement	Corporate Total	Parent plant			Subsidiary plant		
		Total	Products A	B	Total	Products A	B
Sales	3 366 416.65	2 060 500.-	710 500.-	1 350 000.-	1 305 916.65	615 916.65	690 000.-
Less: variable selling costs	66 055.83	41 210.-	14 210.-	27 000.-	24 845.83	11 345.83	13 500.-
Net sales	3 300 360.82	2 019 290.-	696 290.-	1 323 000.-	1 281 070.82	604 570.82	676 500.-
Less: standard costs of goods sold	1 757 287.49	1 038 550.-	375 550.-	663 000.-	718 737.49	345 237.49	373 500.-
Contribution	1 543 073.33	980 740.-	320 740.-	660 000.-	562 333.33	259 333.33	303 000.-
Less: interest expenses	7 612.-						
Value of objective function	1 535 461.33						
Less: Fixed Costs	1 465 000.-	915 000.-			550 000.-		
Profit before tax	70 461.33	65 740.-			12 333.33		
Income tax	35 230.67						
Net operating profit	35 230.66						

Table 2-22. Projected Income Statement.

71

solution indicates that transportation of finished products will take place between the plants, we must have separate lines for the sending and receiving of products in the production budget. The cash budget can only be drawn up for the firm as a whole. The development of these budgets is left to the reader as an exercise.

Assets					
Current Assets					
Cash			100 000		
Accounts Receivable					
Parent					
A	71 050				
B	66 000	137 050			
Subsidiary					
A (3.80–3.42) 162 083.3	61 591.67				
B (4.60–4.37) 150 000	34 500	96 091.67		233 141.67	333 141.67 ·
Inventories					
Raw Materials					
Parent					
W	8 250				
U	21 200	29 450			
Subsidiary					
W (0.15)18 000	2 700				
U (0.265)27 000	7 155	9 855	39 305		
Work in Process					
Parent		87 900			
Subsidiary		9 100	97 000		
Finished Products					
Parent					
A	46 250				
B	61 880	108 130			
Subsidiary					
A (2.13)18 000	38 340				
B (2.49) 13 500	33 615	71 955	180 085		316 390
Prepaid Expenses					6 200
Fixed Assets					
Beginning Balance	1 058 220				
Acquisitions	250 000		1 308 220		
Depreciation					
Parent		220 000			
Subsidiary		50 000	270 000		1 038 220
Total					$ 1 693 951.67

Liabilities					
Accounts Payable					
Raw Materials					
Parent					
W	6 040				
U	27 450	33 490			
Subsidiary					
W (0.01)478 250	4 782.50				
U (0.045)294 000	13 230	18 012.50	51 502.50		
Wages			78 000		
Accrued Interest			2 612		
Accrued Sales Commissions					
Parent		41 210			
Subsidiary		24 845.83	66 055.83		
Accrued Income Tax			35 230.67		
Other Accounts Payable			37 500	270 901	
Bank Loans					
Long-Term Debt			90 000		
New Loans			26 120	116 120	
Shareholders' Equity					
Share Capital			1 000 000		
Undistributed Profit					
Beginning Balance	291 700				
Dividends	20 000	271 700			
Profit for the Period		35 230.66	306 930.66	1 306 930.66	
Total				$ 1 693 951.66	

Table 2-23. The Projected Corporate Balance Sheet.

Problems

2-1. Glo-Paints, Inc. manufactures paints for both industrial uses and home painting. There is a large number of different shades of colour. Similarly, there are other differences in quality. Also, the cans into which the paints are packed come in different sizes. In principle, we would therefore have to distinguish between a large number of different products. For planning purposes we must aggregate the products in a smaller number of product groups. We assume that at the most aggregate level, there are only two product groups, industrial paints and house paints.

The best sales season is spring and early summer. We are now in the middle of April and the planning of operations for May is now in process. The marketing management estimates that the firm can sell during the month of May at most 3 600 units of industrial paints and 2 000 units of house paints. The sales price free at the factory is $ 450 per unit for the industrial paints. The normal terms of payment call for a 50 per cent down payment on delivery and the remainder during the following month. The sales price of the house paints is somewhat higher, $ 600 per unit, but on the other hand, the financing requirements for this product are much heavier for it is being sold at one period credit.

On the basis of the operations in April the production manager estimates that the ending inventory for the month will be 600 units for industrial paints. The peak sales season is in May and the stocks may be reduced during the month. The required ending inventory for May is therefore only 360 units. The ending inventory of house paints for the month of April is 200 units. Since the peak season for house paints is June, the management requires the May ending balance to be at least 400 units. Work in process is assumed to remain at a constant level during the planning period.

The standard use of raw material is 2 units for each unit of industrial paints and 3 units for a unit of house paints. The beginning balance of raw material is 400 units. The raw material inventory is at an abnormally low level. For this reason the management wants to increase it by the end of May. The required ending balance is 750 units. The standard price of raw material is $ 140 per unit. The terms of payment are 75 per cent down and the rest one month later.

The production is carried out in two departments, mixing and packing departments. Both products go through both departments. The mixing of raw material requires 2.5 standard labor hours for industrial paints and 3 standard labor hours for house paints per unit of product. The packing operation standard time is 0.2 hours per unit of product for both product groups. The total mixing capacity is 13 000 hours and the total packing capacity 1 200 hours in May.

Direct wages and the associated variable overhead costs are $ 12 per standard labor hour in the mixing and $ 8 per standard labor hour in the packing department. The accounting system of the firm is based on the direct standard costing method. In other words, all fixed costs are period costs.

The controller has prepared a fixed overhead cost budget for May. The cost components of the budget are depreciation and other fixed costs. About 80 per cent of the other fixed costs must be paid in cash during the planning period. The remainder is paid in the following month. The fixed cost budget is the following:

Fixed Overhead	Administration	Sales	Production	Total
Depreciation	–	1 500.–	30 000.–	37 500.–
Other	80 000.–	260 000.–	160 000.–	500 000.–
Total	$ 80 000.–	267 500.–	193 000.–	537 500.–

The beginning balance as at the first of May is given below. The accounts receivable balance is the result of the sales in April and it can all be collected during May.

Beginning Balance Sheet

Cash	280 000	Accounts Payable	
Accounts Receivable	1 875 000	Raw Material	1 020 000
Finished Products		Wages	18 650
Industrial Paints	186 960	Fixed Expenses	96 000
House Paints	91 520	Income Tax	150 000
Work in Process	117 100	Bank Loans	1 000 000
Raw Material	56 000	Share Capital	1 200 000
Fixed Assets	1 260 000	Undistributed Profit	381 930
	$ 3 866 580		$ 3 866 580

Raw materials have been purchased in April in accordance with normal payment terms. No changes are expected in the amount of work force. This implies that the balance of accrued wages remains at a constant level over the period. Accrued fixed expenses and income taxes shown in the beginning balance must be paid in May.

Existing bank loans must be amortized to the total of $ 400 000 during May. The interest on these loans has already been taken into account in the budget for fixed expenses. If the firm needs additional financing in May, it may take a new loan. The loan can be any amount up to the limit of $ 600 000. This loan carries an interest of 12 per cent per annum. The loan can be taken against three month bills with interest payable in advance. In the projected income statement we will observe only the interest for the first month.

There are no dividend payments during May. The same is true for new capital expenditures. The cash balance at the end of April is higher than usual. The treasurer estimates that a closing balance of $ 150 000 covers the minimum safety requirements at the end of May. If it turns out that the firm has excessive cash available at the end of the period, it can deposit excess cash in an interest bearing account at 6 per cent interest per annum. This implies an interest of 0.5 per cent over the planning horizon.

The management group has requested your consulting services. You are requested to help them in building a budget model for the firm and implementing it. Because the management as well as the accounting personnel has only had a superficial acquaintance with linear programming applications, they would like you to show in practice how the functional budgets for the various sectors of the firm are developed on the basis of the solution to the model.

The company has an offer of a factoring financing credit up to a limit of $ 100 000. However, the effective cost of this financing is 18 per cent per annum. Although the cost of this financing seems to be prohibitive, the management would like to have your opinion as to the advisability of accepting this offer. This is because the financing position of the firm seems to be very tight. The treasurer has already voiced his opinion and said that it is impossible to accept this offer because of the high costs it entails.

2.2. Table 2-24 presents an optimal solution to the model in Table 2-20 with a slight variation in two coefficients of the model. The changes in the model are the following:

a) The right-hand side coefficient of constraints (2-13) which indicates the available production capacity in the subsidiary plant is now 220 000 hours.
b) It has been assumed in the formulation of constraint (2-15) that 85 % of the sales revenue of product A of the subsidiary is collected in the same period that the subsidiary plant sells the product.

Draw up the plantwise sales, transportation, manufacturing, and purchasing budgets as well as the corporate level cash budget together with the projected financial statements. The differences in standard costs are reflected in the income statement of the receiving plant. The receiving plant also absorbs the cost of transportation between the plants.

2-3. Planning Operations in a Multi-National Firm

1. Outline of the Problem

Assume that we are analyzing a two-plant firm with plants in different countries. The plant located in country A_1 is denoted by T_1, and the plant in country A_2 by T_2. Both plants make the same product. The production involves making a number of parts independently of each other and then assembling them together in an assembly line. Normally a unit of each part goes into the final product. However, there is also a part two units of which are required for a unit of final product.

The parts can be made in both plants. The only effective production constraints are the limited production capacities of the various machine groups in each plant. Labor and raw materials are available in sufficient quantities. There is no joint production of the parts and their machining times stated below have been computed on the basis of "normal" lot sizes including set up times.

The machines in the two plants are of different quality. It follows that each plant has its own set of machining time standards. The same holds true for the standard costs of the two plants. Another aspect of the cost structure due to the multinationality of the firm is that the cost of making a part, say, in plant T_1 for assembly in the same plant is different from the cost of making the same part for assembly in T_2.

VARIABLE	TYPE	ENTRIES	SOLUTION ACTIVITY	UPPER BOUND	LOWER BOUND	CURRENT COST	REDUCED COST
XAP	B*	4	218857.143	**********	0.000	1.580	0.000
CONTRIB	B*	0	1580351.997	**********	**********	-1.000	-1.000
XBP	B*	4	300000.000	**********	0.000	2.200	0.000
TAPS	LL	4	0.000	**********	0.000	-0.580	-0.045
TASP	LL	4	0.000	**********	0.000	-0.020	-0.614
TBPS	B*	4	13214.286	**********	0.000	-0.679	0.000
TBSP	LL	4	0.000	**********	0.000	-0.120	-0.880
XAS	B*	4	179999.999	**********	0.000	1.600	0.000
XBS	B*	4	149999.999	**********	0.000	2.020	0.000
R	B*	2	7456.571	**********	0.000	-1.000	0.000
PSALEA	B*	0	218857.143	250000.000	0.000	0.000	0.000
PINVENA	LL	0	-5000.000	**********	-5000.000	0.000	-1.895
PSALEB	UL	0	300000.000	300000.000	0.000	0.000	-0.360
PINVENB	LL	0	10000.000	**********	10000.000	0.000	-2.267
YAP	B*	4	213857.143	**********	0.000	0.000	0.000
PPRODCA	UL	0	285000.000	285000.000	0.000	0.000	-3.426
PRAWMAW	LL	0	10000.000	**********	10000.000	0.000	-0.014
YBP	B*	4	296785.713	**********	0.000	0.000	0.000
PRAWMAU	LL	0	-10000.000	**********	-10000.000	0.000	-0.021
ZWP	B*	2	651571.430	**********	0.000	0.000	0.000
ZUP	B*	2	583571.429	**********	0.000	0.000	0.000

Table 2-24a. Solution to Problem 2-2, Section 1.

77

SINVENA	LL	0	-2000.000	**********	-2000.000	0.000	-1.330
SINVENB	LL	0	-1500.000	**********	-1500.000	0.000	-1.547
SSALEA	UL	0	180000.000	180000.000	0.000	0.000	-0.592
SSALEB	UL	0	150000.000	150000.000	0.000	0.000	-0.909
YAS	B*	4	177999.999	**********	0.000	0.000	0.000
SPRODCA	UL	0	220000.000	220000.000	0.000	0.000	-1.868
SRAWMAW	LL	0	-2000.000	**********	-2000.000	0.000	-0.014
YBS	B*	4	161714.286	**********	0.000	0.000	0.000
SRAWMAU	LL	0	-3000.000	**********	-3000.000	0.000	-0.021
ZWS	B*	2	532000.000	**********	0.000	0.000	0.000
ZUS	B*	2	320428.572	**********	0.000	0.000	-0.000
CASH	LL	0	1451000.001	**********	1451000.001	0.000	-0.100
V	B*	3	24565.717	**********	0.000	0.000	0.000
DEBTLIM	B*	0	24565.717	50000.000	0.000	0.000	0.000
INTERESTEQ		0	5000.000	5000.000	5000.000	0.000	-1.000

Table 2-24b. Solution to Problem 2-2, Section 2.

The transfer of parts across national boundaries results in transportation costs, duties and taxes which may be different depending on the direction of the movement, i.e. national policies on duties and taxes may differ from one another.

It is also assumed that if the plants cannot jointly produce a sufficient number of a given part the shortage can be covered by subcontracting at a given price which is known in advance.

The sales forecasts indicate that a given number of product is going to be sold both in A_1 and in A_2. The production planning problem is to determine the number of parts to be made and/or purchased in each plant to satisfy the assembly requirements in the two plants minimizing the total costs production and purchasing in the two countries.

2. Data Collection

The necessary data for the formulation of the model has been collected and organized. The results are presented in Tables 2-25 and 2-26. Let us first review the data in Table 2-25. The section for plant T_1, column Parts S_i, designates the various parts $S_1, \ldots, S_4$. The following column lists the variables used in the formulation of the model. For example, variable x_1 represents the number of units of part S_1 to be made in T_1 for assembly in T_1, x_5 the number of units of the same part to be made in T_1 for assembly in T_2, and x_9 the number of units of the part subcontracted in A_1 for assembly in T_1. We assume that the unit used in the model is 1 000 pieces. For example, if the solution indicates that $x_5 = 3$, we know that 3 000 units of part S_1 is produced in plant T_1 for assembly in T_2.

The next column lists the respective variable costs of production and the subcontractors´ prices. The coefficient on the first row in this column, 4, indicates that if we make one unit of part S_1 in T_1 for assembly in T_1, the variable costs are 4 monetary units. Let the monetary unit be $ 10 000, i.e., it costs $ 40 000 to make 1 000 pieces of part S_1. The coefficient associated with variable x_5 is 5. The transportation costs, duties and taxes resulting from the transfer of one unit of part S_1 from T_1 to T_2 are $ 10 000: 4 + 1 = 5. On the other hand, if we subcontract one unit of part S_1 in A_1, the costs are $ 60 000. This is indicated by the coefficient associated with variable x_9.

The remaining three columns of Table 2-25 list the standard machining times and the available capacities of each machine group. Since subcontracting does not require machine capacity, the respective rows have been crossed out. The coefficients on the row associated with variable x_5 are identical to those on the x_1-row. The interpretation is that it takes the same amount of production capacity to make a part for assembly in the same plant, or for export to the sister plant. The unit for production capacity is 1 000 hours. For example, to make 1 000

79

Plant T_1						
Alternative	Parts S_i	Variables x_i	Variable Costs	Machine Groups		
				Lathes	Drilling Machines	Grinding Machines
Production for Assembly in T_1	S_1	x_1	4	5	6	9
	S_2	x_2	8	2	1	3
	S_3	x_3	3	1		5
	S_4	x_4	5		4	2
Production for Assembly in T_2	S_1	x_5	5	5	6	9
	S_2	x_6	10	2	1	3
	S_3	x_7	4	1		5
	S_4	x_8	6		4	2
Subcontracting for Assembly in T_1	S_1	x_9	6			
	S_2	x_{10}	10			
	S_3	x_{11}	3.5			
	S_4	x_{12}	7			
Available Capacity				30	30	48

Plant T_2						
Alternative	Parts S_i	Variables y_i	Variable Costs	Machine Groups		
				Lathes	Drilling Machines	Grinding Machines
Production for Assembly in T_2	S_1	y_1	5	5	5	6
	S_2	y_2	6	2	1	2
	S_3	y_3	4	1		4
	S_4	y_4	4.5		3	2
Production for Assembly in T_1	S_1	y_5	5.5	5	5	6
	S_2	y_6	6.6	2	1	2
	S_3	y_7	4.4	1		4
	S_4	y_8	5		3	2
Subcontracting for Assembly in T_2	S_1	y_9	8			
	S_2	y_{10}	7			
	S_3	y_{11}	5			
	S_4	y_{12}	6			
Available Capacity				60	50	70

Table 2-25. Production and Subcontracting Alternatives, Cost Structure and Capacity Data

pieces of part S_1 we need 5 000 hours of production capacity in the first machine group.

Plant T_1			
	Alternatives		
Parts S_i	Production in T_1	Subcontracting in A_1	Transfer from T_2	Requirements for Assembly
S_1	x_1	x_9	y_5	4
S_2	x_2	x_{10}	y_6	2
S_3	x_3	x_{11}	y_7	2
S_4	x_4	x_{12}	y_8	2

Plant T_2			
	Alternatives		
Parts S_i	Production in T_2	Subcontracting in A_2	Transfer from T_1	Requirements for Assembly
S_1	y_1	y_9	x_5	8
S_2	y_2	y_{10}	x_6	4
S_3	y_3	y_{11}	x_7	4
S_4	y_4	y_{12}	x_8	4

Table 2-26. Assembly Requirements of Parts.

Some parts do not require all types of production capacity. For example, part S_3 does not require any drilling machine capacity. Therefore, there is a zero in the Drilling Machine-column on the S_3-row.

The interpretation of the lower part of Table 2-25 is analogous. Variables y_i represent the production and subcontracting alternatives in plant T_2. Variable costs and standard capacity hours are given in the remaining columns.

As can be seen on the row for available capacity, plant T_2 is almost double the size of plant T_1. This is not true, however, for each machine group. For example, the capacity of grinding machines in T_2 is not twice as large as that in T_1. On the other hand, grinding machines in T_2 seems to be more efficient than in T_1. This can be seen by comparing the respective machining times of individual parts.

The cost data indicates that it is more expensive to export from T_1 to T_2 than to the opposite direction. For example, to make one unit of part S_1 in T_1 costs 4 monetary units if it is for assembly in T_1 and 5 monetary units if it is for assembly in T_2. The cost increase is 25 percent. The respective ratio is 10 percent in plant T_2.

There are also differences in subcontracting prices. For example, part S_1 is more expensive in A_2 than in A_1. The contrary is true with respect to part S_2. This is a typical situation in a case where there are no unified markets for individual parts.

We next turn to Table 2-26. The upper half of that table represents again the situation in plant T_1. The right hand side column of the table indicates the production requirements for each part. The sales forecast for A_1 calls for the production of 2 000 units of the final product. Two units of part S_1 go into a unit of the final product. Therefore, 4 000 units of part S_1 are required to satisfy the assembly line. Only one unit of every other part is required to make the final product. Therefore, the number on every other row in this column is 2.

The other columns of the table indicate the alternative ways to satisfy the assembly requirements. Parts can be made in plant T_1, subcontracted in the host country of T_1, or imported from T_2. The parts acquired in alternative ways must equal the number of parts required by the assembly line.

The interpretation of the lower part of the table is again analogous. The sales forecast fo A_2 is 4 000 units. Therefore, 8 units of part S_1 and 4 units of every other part are needed in the assembly. Again, there are three different strategies for acquiring each part. The sum of parts produced, subcontracted and imported must equal the number of parts required by the assembly plan.

3. Formulation of the Linear Programming Problem

The objective is to minimize the total variable costs of the production and subcontracting in both countries. To write the objective, we multiply the variables in Table 2-25 by the respective cost coefficients and form the sum of the products. The sum, denoted by Z, is to be minimized:

$$\text{Min } Z = 4x_1 + 8x_2 + 3x_3 + 5x_4 + 10x_6 + 4x_7 + 6x_8 + 6x_9 + 10x_{10} +$$
$$(1) \quad 3.5x_{11} + 7x_{12} + 5y_1 + 6y_2 + 4y_3 + 4.5y_4 + 5.5y_5 + 6.6y_6 +$$
$$4.4y_7 + 5y_8 + 8y_9 + 7y_{10} + 5y_{11} + 6y_{12}.$$

The first set of constraints requires that the capacity used in production must not exceed the available capacity for the machine group. We start with the upper section of Table 2-25 and write down the constraints for lathes, drilling machines, and grinding machines:

$$5x_1 + 2x_2 + x_3 \qquad + 5x_5 + 2x_6 + x_7 \qquad \leq 30$$
$$(2) \quad 6x_1 + x_2 \qquad + 4x_4 + 6x_5 + x_6 \qquad + 4x_8 \leq 30$$
$$9x_1 + 3x_2 + 5x_3 + 2x_4 + 9x_5 + 3x_6 + 5x_7 + 2x_8 \leq 80.$$

The corresponding constraints for plant T_2 can be written as

$$5y_1 + 2y_2 + y_3 \qquad + 5y_5 + 2y_6 + y_7 \qquad \leq 60$$
$$(3) \quad 5y_1 + y_2 \qquad + 3y_4 + 5y_5 + y_6 \qquad + 3y_8 \leq 50$$
$$6y_1 + 2y_2 + 4y_3 + 2y_4 + 6y_5 + 2y_6 + 4y_7 + 2y_8 \leq 70.$$

The data in Table 2-26 is utilized to state the constraints which take into account the sales forecasts of final products together with the product structure:

$$
(4) \quad
\begin{array}{llll}
x_1 & + x_9 & + y_5 & = 4 \\
x_2 & + x_{10} & + y_6 & = 2 \\
x_3 & + x_{11} & + y_7 & = 2 \\
x_4 & + x_{12} & + y & = 2 \\
\end{array}
$$

and

$$
\begin{array}{llll}
y_1 & + y_9 & + x_5 & = 8 \\
y_2 & + y_{10} & + x_6 & = 4 \\
y_3 & + y_{11} & + x_7 & = 4 \\
y_4 & + y_{12} & + x_8 & = 4 \\
\end{array}
$$

Finally we need the nonnegativity constraints:

$$(6) \quad x_1, x_2, \ldots, x_{12}; y_1, y_2, \ldots, y_{12} \geq 0.$$

Required:

(a) Solve the problem.
(b) Locate the origin of each part used for final assembly in both plants:
<u>Plant</u>   <u>Part No.</u>   <u>Production</u>   <u>Import</u>   <u>Subcontracting</u>
  ...   .
(c) Compute the average unit cost of the final products in both plants (ignoring the assembly costs).
(d) State the capacity usage and the value of an additional capacity unit in each machine group:

Plant	Machine	Unused Capacity	Cost Decrease/ Additional Unit of Capacity
...	...	...	...

(e) Compute the value of imports from each plant in monetary units used in the model.

2-4. Rewrite the model of problem 2-3 by using a single variable to represent production of a part regardless of whether it is used for assembly in the producing plant or exported to the sister plant. It follows that a separate variable must be used for the export of each part. In other words, the structure of the reformulated model should correspond to that depicted in Table 2-20. The cost coefficients associated with the variables showing the exports are obtained by subtracting the respective coefficients in the column for variable costs in Table 2-25. For example, the coefficient associated with the export of part S_1 from T_1 to T_2 is $5 - 4 = 1$.

2-5. Convert the cost minimization model of problem 2-3 into a contribution maximizing model. Let variable q_1 denote the units sold of the final product in plant T_1 and q_2 the units in plant T_2. The selling price of a unit of the final product is 25 monetary units in A_1 and 26 monetary units in A_2. Assume that the upper limits of sales are 2 units in A_1 and 5 units in A_2. Solve the problem and compare the results with the solution of problem 2-3.

3 A Two-Period Model

Data Collection

In some respects the many period models of a single plant look alike single period multi plant models. Carrying inventories from one period to another and transporting goods from one location to another are related activities. In fact, carrying inventories can be interpreted as transportation of goods from one period to the next. The analogy is not complete, however, in that inventories can only be carried forward in time whereas transportation of goods between two geographic locations can take place into either direction.

There may be several reasons for carrying inventories. Perhaps the most common reason is the seasonality of the demand. Figure 6 depicts a usual situation where the demand exceeds the production capacity in the latter half-year while there is excess capacity in the first half-year. A possible strategy in this situation is to produce for stock in the first half-year and satisfy the excess demand by depleting inventories int the second half-year.

Other reasons for carrying inventories are price variations or an outright discontinuity of the supply of raw materials. Several agricultural products are available only in a given season and cannot be stored as such. If it is possible to store the processed product it is usually advantageous to produce for stock in the season when the raw material is available.

Divergence of production from sales may have important effects on the financial position of the firm. When production exceeds sales, funds are tied into operation. If we draw a budget for the firm considered in Figure 6, and if we consider the budget year as a single period in the cash budget we may come to the conclusion that available funds are sufficient for meeting the requirements of the budget year. Yet the firm may get into financial difficulties after six months because of the peak inventories it is carrying at that point.

The objective of the cash budget is to give the management an early warning of a situation like this and to allow time for the arranging of

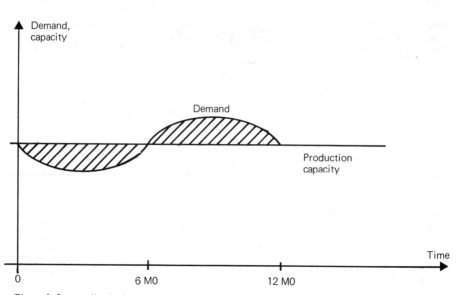

Figure 6. Seasonality in demand vs. stable production capacity.

additional financing, or if this is not possible, for the adjustment of
production to a level which is feasible in relation to financing possibilities.

The seasonality of demand and the changes in the financing needs can
only be taken into account in the model if the total planning horizon is
subdivided into several periods. In addition to the normal data collecting
problems we then must face the problem of determining the appropriate
number of periods. If we subdivide the budget year into many periods
the size of the model increases and the uncertainty about the timing of
cash payments and disbursements is also increased. The relative
magnitude of the error is much smaller if we have to estimate the cash
payments within two months from today than if we have to estimate
the cash payments during the 57th day of the horizon.

In the present chapter we consider an example with two periods only.
In real budget models the year is subdivided into at least three or four
periods. However, a two-period example already demonstrates the
basic features of multi period models. We can therefore avoid the
increase in the size of the example by refraining from the introduction
of additional periods.

In the example of chapter 2 we considered a firm with a single plant
and two products. We now change the original assumptions to show
seasonality in demand. Assume now that the demand for the final
products is as follows:

	Demand	
Product	1st period	2nd period
A	220 000 units	250 000 units
B	300 000 »	300 000 »

Table 3-1. The Demand forecasts of the two products.

The seasonality in demand is concentrated in product A. There may also be seasonal fluctuations in the available production capacity which may be the result of vacations, machine overhaul, etc. In the present example we assume that the available production capacity is 300 000 hours in period 1 and 280 000 hours in period 2.

It is assumed that the target ending balances of raw materials and final products of the original example in chapter 2 now apply to both periods of the present version of the model. The fixed overhead budget of the single period model is now the budget for the first period and the same budget applies again to the second period. The terms of payment both for the sale of final products and for the payment of raw materials purchases as well as overhead can also be applied without modification.

If we assume in a real application that 90 percent of the sales income of the year is collected during the same year we cannot of course assume that 90 percent of the sales income of the first half-year is collected during the same half-year. In this sense there is an inconsistency between the example of chapter 2 and the present example.

This inconsistency is avoided in the treatment of loans. We now assume that the interest on loans is 5 percent per period. The loans existing at the beginning of the first period must be amortized in the amount of $ 5 000 during the first period and $ 4 500 during the second period.

We now assume that if the required minimum cash balance is exceeded the excess funds can be invested outside the firm. The interest income produced by these funds is 3 percent per period and received during the second period for deposits made during the first period. For deposits made in the second period the interest is received only after horizon. This interest bearing investment opportunity is needed in a model which may produce a seasonal cash surplus. If there is no such opportunity the surplus funds may be used in the optimal solution for the purchase of excess stocks of raw materials or some other non-productive purpose.

Since the opportunity costs of funds are now included in the model both for the case when the firm takes new loans and for the case when it invests outside the firm there is no need to include the opportunity costs of funds into the inventory carrying costs. The costs associated with seasonal inventories will therefore include only the storage and obsolescence costs. These costs are assumed to be 6 percent per period in the present example.

Inventory policy can be considered as a policy of balancing carrying and shortage costs. We will not directly consider shortage costs in the present model. The lost contribution on sales foregone is working in the direction of shortage costs, however. It is assumed that if we cannot satisfy all the demand in the first period it will not affect sales in the second period.

The firm might have other strategies available for meeting seasonal demand in addition to production for stock, e.g., overtime work, second shift, and subcontracting. These alternatives will not be considered in the present example.

Formulation of the Model

We begin the formulation of the model by stating the upper limits on sales. The sales of the products are denoted by variables x_A and x_B like before but now a second subscript is needed to identify the period of the model. We get the constraints:

$$(3\text{-}1) \quad \begin{aligned} x_{A1} &\leq 220\ 000 \\ x_{B1} &\leq 300\ 000 \\ x_{A2} &\leq 250\ 000 \\ x_{B2} &\leq 300\ 000. \end{aligned}$$

The next set of constraints relates the beginning balances and the production to the sales and the ending balances of the finished products. The restrictions require that a minimum ending balance must exist for both products at the end of each period. In addition, they allow the existence of seasonal inventories at the end of the first period. There is no need to allow for this possibility at the end of the second period for the model has no way of considering the sales opportunities beyond the horizon. The seasonal inventories are denoted by variables i_{A1} and i_{B1}.

$$(3-2) \quad \begin{aligned} 30\ 000 + y_{A1} &= x_{A1} + i_{A1} + 25\ 000 \\ 18\ 000 + y_{B1} &= x_{B1} + i_{B1} + 28\ 000 \\ i_{A1} + 25\ 000 + y_{A2} &= x_{A2} + 25\ 000 \\ i_{B1} + 28\ 000 + y_{B2} &= x_{B2} + 28\ 000 \end{aligned}$$

The production capacity constraints both relate to a single period because it is impossible to transfer the unutilized capacity of the first period to be utilized in the second period:

$$(3-3) \quad \begin{aligned} 0.5y_{A1} + 0.6y_{B1} &\leq 300\ 000 \\ 0.5y_{A2} + 0.6y_{B2} &\leq 280\ 000. \end{aligned}$$

We assume that a sufficient amount of raw material is available in each period. The prices of raw materials are also assumed to remain constant over the horizon. Therefore, there is no need to anticipate seasonal inventories of raw materials in the present example. The constraints relating the beginning balances and the purchases to materials used in production and the required ending balances can be written as

$$(3-4) \quad \begin{aligned} 45\ 000 + z_{W1} &\geq 3y_{A1} + 55\ 000 \\ 90\ 000 + z_{U1} &\geq 2y_{B1} + 80\ 000 \\ 55\ 000 + z_{W2} &\geq 3y_{A2} + 55\ 000 \\ 80\ 000 + z_{U2} &\geq 2y_{B2} + 80\ 000. \end{aligned}$$

Variable m_1 which represents the cash in excess of the required minimum ending balance of $\$100\ 000$ is added to the cash constraint of the 1st period. This variable transfers the excess cash of the first period into the 2nd period via deposit in an interest bearing account outside the firm for one period. Similarly, variable m_2 represents the excess cash at the end of the second period.

$$(3-5) \quad \begin{aligned} &3.15x_{A1} + 4.28x_{B1} - 1.40y_{A1} - 1.68y_{B1} - 0.14z_{W1} \\ &- 0.22z_{U1} + v_1 - m_1 = 951\ 000 \\[6pt] &0.28x_{A1} + 0.13x_{B1} - 0.01z_{W1} - 0.045z_{U1} - 0.25v_1 - \\ &- n_1 + 1.03m_1 + 3.15x_{A2} + 4.28x_{B2} - 1.40y_{A2} - \\ &- 1.68y_{B2} - 0.14z_{W2} - 0.22z_{U2} + v_2 - m_2 = 729\ 500. \end{aligned}$$

The first period constraint is the same as in the model of chapter 2 except for variable m_1. The constraint is now an equality because m_1 takes care of all the excess cash.

The second period constraint deserves more comments. Since money can be carried forward in time, the constraint for the second period must take into account all cash payments and receipts from the beginning of the first period to the end of the second period. Variable m_1 transfers the excess cash from the first to the second period in the form of an interest bearing deposit. However, there are also other first period variables which enter the second period constraint.

A part of the first period sales revenue is received in the second period. We also assume that the commission on the first period sales is paid in the second period. In the case of product A we receive the difference between the selling price and the amount collected in the first period: $(3.50 - 3.15)x_{A1}$. The sales commission is $0.07x_{A1}$. Therefore, the net effect to the cash position is $(3.50 - 3.15 - 0.07)x_{A1} = 0.28x_{A1}$. Similarly, the net effect of the first period sales of product B is $(4.50 - 4.28 - 0.09)x_{B1} = 0.13x_{B1}$.

A part of the raw material purchases of the first period are unpaid at the beginning of the second period. The net effect is again the difference between the purchase price and the amount paid in the first period: $(0.15 - 0.14)z_{W1} = 0.01z_{W1}$ and $(0.265 - 0.22)z_{U1} = 0.045z_{U1}$.

The loan taken in the first period must be amortized in the second period. The repayment is 20 percent of the principal. In addition, we assume that 5 percent interest must be paid together with the amortization. The total cash payment in the second period relating to the first period loan is therefore $0.25v_1$.

We assume that the income tax rate is 50 percent. It follows that the income tax equals the net operating profit. Variable n_j can be used both for the income tax and for the operating profit and the profit before tax is $2n_j$. The second period constraint must take into account the payment of the income tax of the first period. This is done by subtracting variable n_1 from the left-hand side.

Finally we must take into account the excess cash at the end of the first period together with the interest earned on it. The second period cash is therefore increased by the deposit m_1 and interest earned on it $0.03m_1$.

The remaining second period terms $3.15x_{A2} + 4.28x_{B2} - 1.40y_{A2} - 1.68y_{B2} - 0.14z_{W2} - 0.22z_{U2} + v_2 - m_2$ refer to second period transactions which cause cash payments and receipts in the same period. They all have their corresponding terms in the first period constraint. Variable m_2 collects all excess cash in the second period and invests it outside the firm in an interest bearing account.

The constant on the right hand side of the second period constraint is formultated by taking into account all fixed cash payments and receipts.

In the present example there are no fixed second period cash receipts other than the minimum cash balance of the first period, $ 100 000. Overhead expenses, amortization and interest of old loans and dividends give rise to fixed cash expenses in the second period:

Fixed cash receipts				
Minimum ending balance of the first period			100 000	
Fixed cash expenses				
Fixed overhead				
Sales	250 000			
Administration	290 000			
Production	155 000	695 000		
Existing loans				
Amortization	10 000			
Interest	4 500	14 500		
Dividends		20 000	729 500	
Minimum ending balance of the 2nd period			100 000	829 500
Fixed net expenses				$ 729 500

An alternative way to write the second period cash constraint would be the following:

$$3.43x_{A1} + 4.41x_{B1} - 1.40y_{A1} - 1.68y_{B1} - 0.15z_{W1} - 0.265z_{U1} +$$
$$+ 0.75v_1 - n_1 + 0.03m_1 + 3.15x_{A2} + 4.28x_{B2} - 1.40y_{A2} - 1.68y_{B2} -$$
$$- 0.14z_{W2} - 0.22z_{U2} + v_2 - m_2 = 1\ 680\ 500.$$

This is the sum of the constraints in (3-5). For example, the coefficient of the first period loan shows the effect of the loan from the beginning of the first period to the end of the second period: $(+1 - 0.2 - 0.05)v_1 = 0.75v_1$. When the loan is taken in the first period, the cash position is improved. On the other hand, the payment of amortization and interest drain cash in the second period. Similarly, the coefficient of the excess cash balance shows the net effect of the deposit:

$$(-1 + 1 + 0.03)m_1 = 0.03m_1.$$

The payment of income taxes in the second period depends on the first period profit which is not known before the solution of the model. The following constraints compute the profit before tax for both periods:

(3-6)
$$1.58x_{A1} + 2.20x_{B1} + 0.03m_1 - r_1 - 915\ 000 = 2n_1$$
$$1.58x_{A2} + 2.20x_{B2} + 0.03m_2 - r_2 - 915\ 000 = 2n_2$$

We add to the total contribution, $1.58x_{Aj} + 2.20x_{Bj}$, the interest income, $0.03m_j$, and deduct the interest expenses, r_j, as well as the fixed overhead, $ 915 000. The fixed overhead includes of course the depreciation of fixed assets. The profit before tax, $2n_j$, results in the payment of the income tax, n_j, in the $j+1^{th}$ period.

We do not actually need the second constraint in (3-6) in the present example because the second period income tax, n_2, is paid only after the horizon. It is also worth noting that the inventory carrying costs are not reflected in (3-6). Inventory carrying costs are a subjective cost item not reflected in the accounting entries which are the basis for income taxes.

It is assumed that the creditors of the firm have set upper limits to the amount of new loans which can be taken. The first period loans can be any amount up to $ 50 000. The sum of the first and second period loans outstanding at the end of the second period must not exceed $ 100 000:

$$
\begin{array}{ll}
(3\text{-}7) & v_1 \le 50\ 000 \\
& 0.8v_1 + v_2 \le 100\ 000.
\end{array}
$$

The terms of the loans call for repayment of the principal in instalments of 20 percent in each period following the period when the loan is taken. Therefore, the outstanding amount of the first period loan at the end of the second period is $(1 - 0.2)v_1 = 0.8v_1$. The total of new loans outstanding at the ned of the second period is therefore $0.8v_1 + v_2$.

The total interest expenses of the first period are the sum of the interest on old loans, $ 5 000, and the 5 percent interest on new loans, $0.05v_1$. The interest on old loans in the second period is $ 4 500. The interest on new loans must account for the loans taken both in the first and in the second period. Only 80 percent of the first period loan remains unpaid in the second period. The equations are therefore

$$
\begin{array}{ll}
(3\text{-}8) & r_1 = 5\ 000 + 0.05v_1 \\
& r_2 = 4\ 500 + 0.05(0.8)v_1 + 0.05v_2.
\end{array}
$$

Variables r_1 and r_2 are defined on an accrual basis. The payment of the interest on new loans takes place in the period following the recording of the respective expenses.

The objective function includes the contribution, interest expenses and the inventory carrying costs as well as the interest income on the excess cash:

$$\text{Max } Z = 1.58x_{A1} + 2.20x_{B1} - r_1 - 0.11i_{A1} - 0.13i_{B1} + 0.03m_1 +$$
$$+ 1.58x_{A2} + 2.20x_{B2} - r_2 + 0.03m_2.$$

The seasonal inventory carrying costs were assumed to be 6 percent of the value of inventories, i.e., $0.11i_{A1}$ and $0.13i_{B1}$ are 6 percent of $1.85i_{A1}$ and $2.21i_{B1}$ respectively.

The model has been restated in Table 3-2. The top row shows the objective function. The constraints referring to the first period are listed in the next section. The second period constraints are finally stated in the lower part of the table. The left-hand side of the table shows the variables referring to th first period and the right-hand side the variables for the second period. The variables for the seasonal inventories and the excess cash balance are stated in the middle.

When we compare the layout of this model to the two-plant model of Table 2-20 we note a slight difference in the general structure. The nature of this difference is outlined in Figures 7 and 8. The incomlete analogy is due to the financial constraints of the second period. If Table 3-2 were rearranged in such a way that the financial constraints of both periods were listed at the bottom of the table the physical part of the model would be completely analogous to the two-plant model.

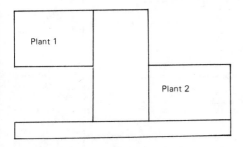

Figure 7. The Basic Structure of the Two-Plant Model.

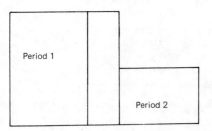

Figure 8. The Basic Structure of the Single-Plant Two-Period Model.

Table 3-2. A Two-Period Budget Model.

	XA1	XB1	YA1	YB1	ZW1	ZU1	V1	RE1	NOE1	IA1	IB1	M1	XA2	XB2	YA2	YB2	ZW2	ZU2	V2	RE2	NOE2	M2	REL	RESTRIC
CONTRIB	1.58	2.20						-1		-0.1	-0.13	0.03	1.58	2.20						-1.		0.03		
SALESA1	1.																						≤	220 000.
SALESB1		1.																					≤	300 000.
INVENA1	-1.		1.							-1.													≥	-5 000.
INVENB1		-1.		1.							-1.												≥	10 000.
PRODCAP1			0.5	0.6																			≤	300 000.
RAWMATW1				-2.	1.																		≥	10 000.
RAWMATU1			-3.			1.																	≥	-10 000.
CASH1	3.15	4.28	-1.40	-1.68	-0.14	-0.22	1.					-1.											=	951 000.
PROFIT1	1.58	2.20						-1.	-2.			0.03											=	915 000.
DEBTLIM1							1.	1.															≤	50 000.
INTREST1							-0.05																=	5 000.
SALESA2													1.										≤	250 000.
SALESB2														1.									≤	300 000.
INVENA2										1.			-1.		1.								≥	0.
INVENB2											1.			-1.		1.							≥	0.
PRODCAP2															0.5	0.6							≤	280 000.
RAWMATW2																-2.	1.						≥	0.
RAWMATU2															-3.			1.					≥	0.
CASH2	0.28	0.13			0.01	-0.045	-0.25		-1.			1.03	3.15	4.28	-1.40	-1.68	-0.14	-0.22	1.			-1.	=	**729 500**
PROFIT2													1.58	2.20						-1.	-2.	0.03	=	915 000.
DEBTLIM2							0.8												1.	1.			≤	100 000.
INTREST2							-0.04												-0.05				=	4 500.

Analysis of the Optimal Solution

The optimal solution of the two-period model is presented in Table 3-3. As can be seen, the available production capacity is used to satisfy the demand for product B completely. Also, the demand for product A is completely satisfied in the first period:

$$x_{A1} = 220\ 000, \quad x_{A2} = 213\ 000,$$
$$x_{B1} = 300\ 000, \quad x_{B2} = 300\ 000.$$

The production capacity available in the first period exceeds the capacity required for satisfying the demand in the same period. It turns out to be advantageous to buid seasonal inventories for the second period sales:

$$i_{A1} = 0,$$
$$i_{B1} = 10\ 833.33.$$

The interesting feature of the seasonal inventories is the fact that product B is being carried in seasonal inventory from the first into the second period, although it is the demand for product A which cannot be satisfied in the second period. A superficial analysis of the problem data might lead into a decision to carry product A in seasonal inventory and to make enough of product B in each period.

The excess cash balance is zero at the end of the first period. However, the situation is different at the end of the second period:

$$m_1 = 0,$$
$$m_2 = 236\ 531.67.$$

In fact, there is a shortage of funds in the first period and new loans are taken in the amount of $ 44 666.67:

$$v_1 = 44\ 666.67,$$
$$v_2 = 0.$$

The solution is consistent. Whenever new loans are needed, there are no excess funds, and whenever there are excess funds, no new loans are taken.

The variable name used for the first period net operating profit in

VARIABLE TYPE	ENTRIES	SOLUTION ACTIVITY	UPPER BOUND	LOWER BOUND	CURRENT COST	REDUCED COST
XA1 B*	6	219999.998	***********	0.000	1.580	0.000
CONTRIB B*	0	1996307.614	***********	***********	-1.000	-1.000
XB1 B*	6	300000.000	***********	0.000	2.199	0.000
RE1 B*	3	7233.333	***********	0.000	-1.000	0.000
IA1 LL	3	0.000	***********	0.000	-0.110	-0.003
IB1 B*	3	10833.335	***********	0.000	-0.129	0.000
M1 LL	4	0.000	***********	0.000	0.030	-0.036
XA2 B*	5	213000.002	***********	0.000	1.580	0.000
XB2 B*	5	300000.000	***********	0.000	2.200	0.000
RE2 B*	3	6286.666	***********	0.000	-1.000	0.000
M2 B*	3	236531.673	***********	0.000	0.030	0.000
SALESA1 UL	0	220000.000	220000.000	0.000	0.000	-0.301
INVENA1 LL	0	-5000.000	***********	-5000.000	0.000	-1.568
CASH1 EQ	0	951000.000	951000.000	951000.000	0.000	-0.096
PROFIT1 EQ	0	915000.000	915000.000	915000.000	0.000	0.015
CASH2 EQ	0	729500.000	729500.000	729500.000	0.000	-0.029
SALESB1 UL	0	300000.000	300000.000	0.000	0.000	-0.707
INVENB1 LL	0	10000.000	***********	10000.000	0.000	-1.877
YA1 B*	4	214999.999	***********	0.000	0.000	0.000
PRODCAP1UL	0	300000.000	300000.000	0.000	0.000	-2.782
RAWMATW1LL	0	10000.000	***********	10000.000	0.000	-0.013
YB1 B*	4	320833.334	***********	0.000	0.000	0.000
RAWMATU1LL	0	-10000.000	***********	-10000.000	0.000	-0.022
ZW1 B*	3	655000.003	***********	0.000	0.000	0.000
ZU1 B*	3	631666.668	***********	0.000	0.000	-0.000
V1 B*	6	44666.669	***********	0.000	0.000	0.000
DEBTLIM1B*	0	44666.669	50000.000	0.000	0.000	0.000
INTREST1EQ	0	5000.000	5000.000	5000.000	0.000	-0.985
DEBTLIM2B*	0	35733.335	100000.000	0.000	0.000	0.000
INTREST2EQ	0	4500.000	4500.000	4500.000	0.000	-1.000
NOE1 B*	2	42683.331	***********	0.000	0.000	0.000
INVENA2 LL	0	0.000	***********	0.000	0.000	-1.674
INVENB2 LL	0	0.000	***********	0.000	0.000	-2.007
SALESA2 B*	0	213000.002	250000.000	0.000	0.000	0.000
PROFIT2 EQ	0	915000.000	915000.000	915000.000	0.000	0.000
SALESB2 UL	0	300000.000	300000.000	0.000	0.000	-0.320
YA2 B*	4	213000.002	***********	0.000	0.000	0.000
PRODCAP2UL	0	280000.000	280000.000	0.000	0.000	-3.239
RAWMATW2LL	0	0.000	***********	0.000	0.000	-0.004
YB2 B*	4	289166.665	***********	0.000	0.000	0.000
RAWMATU2LL	0	0.000	***********	0.000	0.000	-0.006
ZW2 B*	2	639000.006	***********	0.000	0.000	-0.000
ZU2 B*	2	578333.330	***********	0.000	0.000	0.000
V2 LL	3	0.000	***********	0.000	0.000	-0.020
NOE2 B*	1	41174.643	***********	0.000	0.000	0.000

Table 3-3. Optimal Solution of the Two-Period Model.

Table 3-3 is NOE1 and for the second period profit NOE2. The values of these variables are $ 42 683.33 and $ 41 174.64. The variables for production and purchases of raw materials take values which exactly satisfy the sales and inventory requirements.

Development of Budgets

The development of the various budgets follows the procedure of chapter 2. Sales, production, inventory, and purchasing budgets can be developed directly for both periods. The same is true for the cash budget. The projected income statement can be drawn up either for the budget year as a whole or separately for both periods. The projected balance sheet can be developed for the end of every period.

Table 3-4 shows the sales budget separately for each period. The values of variables x_{Aj} and x_{Bj} give the budgeted sales of both products.

1st period	Total $	Price	Product A Quantity	$	Price	Product B Quantity	$
Sales	2 120 000	3.5	220 000	770 000	4.5	200 000	1 350 000
Less: Variable Selling Costs	42 400	0.07		15 400	0.09		27 000
Net Sales	2 077 600			754 600			1 323 000
Less: Standard Cost of Sales	1 070 000	1.85		407 000	2.21		663 000
Contribution	1 007 600			347 600			660 000
2nd period Sales	2 095 500	3.50	213 000	745 500	4.5	300 000	1 350 000
Less: Variable Selling Costs	41 910	0.07		14 910	0.09		27 000
Net Sales	2 053 590			730 590			1 323 000
Less: Standard Cost of Sales	1 057 050	1.85		394 050	2.21		663 000
Contribution	996 540			336 540			660 000

Table 3-4. Sales Budgets.

The production and inventory budgets are presented in Table 3-5. In addition to the values of variables x_{Aj}, x_{Bj}, y_{Aj}, and y_{Bj} as well as the beginning balances and the required ending balances we must now observe the values of variables i_{A1} and i_{B1}. The optimal value of i_{A1} is zero. It follows that the balance of product A at the end of the 1st period is 25 000 units. This is also the beginning balance of the 2nd period. There is no change in the required balance at the end of the 2nd period. Therefore, it is also 25 000 units. The optimal value of i_{B1} is 10 833.33 units. It follows that the total inventory of product B at the end of the 1st period is the required minimum balance, 28 000 units, plus the seasonal inventory, 10 833.33 units, or 38 833.33 units in total.

	1st Period	2nd Period
Product A		
Desired Ending Inventory	25 000	25 000
Plus: Seasonal Inventory	$i_{A1} =$ 0	–
Sales	$x_{A1} =$ 220 000	$x_{A2} =$ 213 000
Total Requirements	245 000	238 000
Less: Beginning Inventory	30 000	25 000
Required Production	$y_{A1} =$ 215 000	$y_{A2} =$ 213 000
Product B		
Desired Ending Inventory	28 000	28 000
Plus: Seasonal Inventory	$i_{B1} =$ 10833.33	–
Sales	$x_{B1} =$ 300 000	$x_{B2} =$ 300 000
Total Requirements	338 833.33	328 000
Less: Beginning Inventory	18 000	38 833.33
Required Production	$y_{B1} =$ 320 833.33	$y_{B2} =$ 289 166.67

Table 3-5. Production and Inventory Budgets.

There are no seasonal inventories of raw materials. The development of purchasing budgets is therefore straight-forward:

	1st Period	2nd Period
Item W		
Desired Ending Inventory	55 000	55 000
Plus: Production Requirements	$3y_{A1} =$ 645 000	$3y_{A2} =$ 639 000
Total Requirements	700 000	694 000
Less: Beginning Balance	45 000	55 000
Required Purchases	$z_{W1} =$ 655 000	$z_{W2} =$ 639 000
Item U		
Desired Ending Inventory	80 000	80 000
Plus: Production Requirements	$2y_{B1} =$ 641 666.67	$2y_{B2} =$ 578 333.33
Total Requirements	721 666.67	658 333.33
Less: Beginning Balance	90 000	80 000
Required Purchases	$z_{U1} =$ 631 666.67	$z_{U2} =$ 578 333.33

Table 3-6. Budgeted Raw Material Purchases.

Cash budget has been presented in Table 3-7. It follows the ordinary budgeting routine except for the slight variation in that both cash receipts and cash expenses have been subdivied into fixed and variable items. The source of variable cash receipts is the sales budget. The first period sales generate cash receipts in both periods. The second period sales are only partially collected in that period. The rest remains in accounts receivable of the projected ending balance for that period.

The first period sales commissions are paid in the second period. The first period income tax is also paid in the second period. Other variable cash expenses are caused by production and raw material purchases.

The beginning cash balance plus cash receipts less cash expenditures from operations gives the cash balance before loans. Subtracting the amortization and interest of existing loans gives the need for new loans in order to get to the desired ending balance. The cash budget has been deliberately drawn up in the way it is being done in traditional budgeting. The upper sections are the result of other budgets and the bottom section is drawn up by the financial department. When we use a linear programming budget model we can of course draw up the cash budget in whatever order we desire because operations and financing are simultaneously taken care of. New short-term loans are no longer mere balancing devices the magnitude of which is decided only after all other budgets have been drawn up.

Table 3-8 shows the projected income statements for both periods. The sales budget gives the sales and the contribution at standard cost. The next line did not appear in the preceding examples of single period budgets because the underlying models did not include the possibility of investing surplus funds outside the firm in an interest bearing account. The interest income on the surplus funds of the second period is reflected in Table 3-8. The net operating profit of both periods agrees with the values of variables NOE1 and NOE2 in Table 3-3.

The subjective inventory carrying costs associated with variables i_{A1} and i_{B1} reduce the optimal value of the objective function. These subjective costs cannot be deducted from the operating profit. The value of the objective function and the profit before fixed costs can be reconciled by deducting the subjective inventory carrying costs:

$$1\ 000\ 366.67 + 997\ 349.28 - (0.13)10\ 833.33 = 1\ 996\ 307.61.$$

Tables 3-9a and 3-9b present the projected balance sheets. The first period balance sheet follows closely the ending balance of the single-period model. The slight differences in accrued interest expenses, accrued income taxes, and the net operating profit are due to changed assumptions about the rate of interest.

The starting point of the second period ending balance is the projected balance for the first period. The assets include the accrued interest income which was observed in the projected income statement for the second period. The ending balance of the existing long-term loans is $ 80 000, since there have been two amortization payments by the end of the second period. The new loans in the first period are $ 44 666.67.

99

	1st Period	2nd Period
Beginning Cash Balance	112 000	100 000
Cash Receipts from Operations		
Fixed		
Accounts Receivable Balance	100 000	
Variable		
Sales		
X_{A1}: (3.15)220 000; (0.35)220 000	693 000	77 000
X_{B1}: (4.28)300 000; (0.22)300 000	1 284 000	66 000
X_{A2}: (3.15)213 000		670 000
X_{B2}: (4.28)300 000		1 284 000
Total Receipts from Operations	2 087 000	2 097 950
Cash Available	2 199 000	2 197 950
Cash Expenditures		
Fixed		
Accounts Payable Balance	93 000	
Dividends	20 000	20 000
Investment Budget	250 000	
Fixed Expenses	695 000	695 000
Variable		
Sales Commissions		42 400
Income Taxes		42 683.33
Production		
Y_{Ai}: (1.40)215 000; (1.40)213 000	301 000	298 200
Y_{Bj}: (1.68)320 833.33; (1.68)289 166.67	539 000	485 800
Raw Material Purchases		
Z_{W1}: (0.14)655 000; (0.01)655 000	91 700	6 550
Z_{U1}: (0.22)631 666.67; (0.045)631 666.67	138 966.67	28 425
Z_{W2}: (0.14)639 000		89 460
Z_{U2}: (0.22)578 333.33		127 233.33
Cash Expenditures for Operations	2 128 666.67	1 835 751.66
Balance Before Loans	55 333.33	362 198.33
Long Term Loans: Amortization	10 000	10 000
Interest	5 000	4 500
New Loans: Principal	44 666.67	
Repayment		8 933.33
Interest		2 233.33
Ending Cash Balance	100 000	336 531.67

Table 3-7. Cash budget.

	1st Period	2nd Period
Sales	2 120 000	2 095 500
Less: Variable Selling Costs	42 400	41 910
Net Sales	2 077 600	2 053 590
Less: Standard Cost of Sales	1 070 000	1 057 050
Contribution	1 007 600	996 540
Interest Income	–	7 095.95
Subtotal	1 007 600	1 003 635.95
Interest Expense	7 233.33	6 286.67
Profit before Fixed Expenses	1 000 366.67	997 349.28
Less: Fixed Expenses	915 000	915 000
Profit before Taxes	85 366.67	82 349.28
Income Tax	42 683.33	41 174.64
Net Operating Profit	42 683.33	41 174.64

Table 3-8. Projected Income Statements.

Assets				
Current Assets				
Cash			100 000	
Accounts Receivable				
A: (0.35) 220 000		77 000		
B: (0.22) 300 000		66 000	143 000	243 000
Inventories				
Raw Materials				
W: (0.15) 55 000		8 250		
U: (0.265) 80 000		21 200	29 450	
Work in Process			87 900	
Finished Products				
A: (1.85) 25 000		46 250		
B: (2.21) 38 833.33		85 821.66	132 071.66	249 421.66
Prepaid Expenses				6 200
Fixed Assets				
Beginning Balance		1 058 000		
Acquisitions		250 000	1 308 220	
Depreciation			220 000	1 088 220
Total Assets				$ 1 586 841.66
Liabilities				
Accounts Payable				
Raw Materials				
W: (0.01) 655 000		6 550		
U: (0.045) 631 666.67		28 425	34 975	
Accrued Wages			78 000	
Accrued Interest			2 233.33	
Accrued Commissions			42 400	
Accrued Income Tax			42 683.33	
Other Accounts Payable			37 500	237 791.66
Loans				
Beginning Balance		100 000		
Repayments		10 000	90 000	
New Loans			44 666.67	134 666.67
Equity				
Shareholder's Capital			900 000	
Undistributed Profit	291 700			
Dividends	20 000	271 700		
Profit for the Period		42 683.33	314 383.33	1 214 383.33
Total Liabilities				$ 1 586 841.66

Table 3-9 a. Projected balance sheet for the first period.

The amortization in the second period is 20 percent of the principal or $ 8 933.33. The outstanding balance at the end of the second period is therefore $ 35 733.34. Accrued interest in the second period balance sheet has been computed on this amount.

Assets				
Current Assets			336 531.67	
Cash and Deposits				
Accounts Receivable				
A: (0.35) 213 000		74 550		
B: (0.22) 300 000		66 000	140 550	477 081.67
Inventories				
Raw Materials				
W: (0.15) 55 000		8 250		
U: (0.265) 80 000		21 200	29 450	
Work in Process			87 900	
Finished Products				
A: (1.85) 25 000		46 250		
B: (2.21) 28 000		61 880	108 130	225 480
Accruals and Prepaid Items				
Accrued Interest			7 095.95	
Prepaid Expenses			6 200	13 295.95
Fixed Assets				
Beginning Balance			1 088 220	
Depreciation			220 000	868 220
Total Assets				$ 1 584 077.62

Liabilities				
Accounts Payable				
Raw Materials				
S: (0.01) 639 000		6 390		
U: (0.045) 578 333.33		26 025	32 415	
Accrued Wages			78 000	
Accrued Interest			1 786.67	
Accrued Commissions			41 910	
Accrued Income Tax			41 174.64	
Other Accounts Payable			37 500	232 786.31
Loans				
Long Term				
Beginning Balance		90 000		
Repayments		10 000	80 000	
New Loans				
Beginning Balance		44 666.67		
Repayments		8 933.33	35 733.34	115 733.34
Equity				
Shareholders' Capital			900 000	
Undistributed Profit				
Beginning Balance	314 383.33			
Dividends	20 000	294 383.33		
Profit for the Period		41 174.64	335 557.97	1 235 557.97
Total Liabilities				$ 1 584 072.62

Table 3-9b. Projected balance sheet for the second period.

Analysis of Shadow Prices

The way the objective function is formulated must be taken into account in the analysis of shadow prices. For example, the shadow price associated with the production capacity of the second period is in accordance with Table 3-3 $ 3. 239 per hour. The only possibility to use an additional hour in the present example is to produce more units of product A. The contribution of product A is $ 1.58 per unit and the required production capacity is 0.5 hours per unit. It would therefore seem that an additional capacity hour would produce an increase of 2(1.58) = $ 3.16 in the objective function. The difference between the value of the shadow price and this figure is the result of financial effects. Two additional units of product A increase the amount of available cash which can be invested at a return of 3 percent per period. The shadow price shows the cumulative effects of the increase in the contribution and the interest income. Since we were discussing the shadow price of a second period constraint the cumulative effects are limited to the second period which also the last period of the model.

Let us next analyze the shadow price associated with the cash constraint of the first period. According to Table 3-3 this is $ 0.096 per $. If the required minimum cash balance were reduced by one dollar from $ 100 000 to $ 99 999 there would be an additional dollar available for financing the operations and the value of the objective function would be increased by $ 0.096. The need for new loans in the first period would be reduced by one dollar. This would reduce the interest expenses by $ 0.05 in the first period and $ 0.04 in the second period. In addition, the second period amortization of the first period loan could be invested outside the firm and would produce an interest income of (0.2)0.03 = = $ 0.006. The cumulative effect of these changes is 0.05 + 0.04 + + 0.006 = $ 0.096 per $. The shadow price of the liquidity constraint shows the cumulative effect of all changes from the period of the constraint to the end period which in this example is the second period.

Table 3-3 also shows that if the required minimum cash balance of the second period were reduced by one dollar the value of the objective function would increase by $ 0.03 (because of rounding, the figure in Table 3-3 is $ 0.029). The best available opportunity to use an additional dollar in the second period would be to invest it outside the firm and this would bring an increase of $ 0.03 in the interest income.

The demand for product B is at the same level in both periods. Yet the shadow price associated with the upper limit of the first period sales is $ 0.707 per unit while the corresponding second period figure is $ 0.32 per unit. The difference is again due to financial effects. If the marketing expenses to increase demand for product B by one unit were equal in both periods then it would be advisable to concentrate the marketing efforts to the first period.

Problems

3-1. Glo-Paints, Inc. introduced in problem 2-1 has gained experience in the use of a single period budget model. The management now wants to develop a model which can better take into account the seasonality in demand. We are again in the middle of April. This time the management wants to plan the operations for both May and June.

The marketing management has developed the sales forecasts. It is expected that the firm could sell 3 600 units of industrial paints in May and 4 000 units in June. The demand for house paints is 2 000 units per month both in May and in June. The sales price is $ 450 per unit for industrial paints ans $ 600 per unit for house paints. The terms of payment are still the same as in problem 2-1.

The ending inventory of industrial paints is 600 units in April. The desired minimum inventory for the month of May is 360 units and for June 450 units. The ending inventory of house paints in April is 200 units. The desired minimum inventory for May is 400 units and for June 300 units. Work in process is assumed to remain at a constant level over the horizon.

The standard use, prices, and terms of payment of raw materials have not changed from problem 2-1. The ending balance of raw materials in April is 400 units. The desired ending balance is 750 units in May and 600 units in June.

The standard labor hours in both mixing and packing remain at their previous level. The production capacity of the packing department is 1 200 hours per month in both periods. The normal capacity of the mixing department is 13 000 hours per month. If necessary, it is also possible to schedule overtime work in the mixing department. The maximum amount of overtime hours is 2 000 hours per moth in both months.

The wage standards also remain unchanged. The direct wages and variable overhead are $ 12 per hour in the mixing and $ 8 per hour in the packing department. The overhead bonus in the mixing department is $ 6 per hour. In cost accounting the overtime bonus is treated like the fixed overhead and charged directly against the income for the period without carrying it into inventory as product costs.

The budget for the fixed selling, administration, and manufacturing overhead is $ 537 500 per month in both months. The depreciation and payment practices have not changed.

The beginning balance sheet as at the first of May is the same as in problem 2-1. Bank loans shown in the beginning balance must be amortized in the amount of $ 400 000 in May. There are no amortization payments in June and no interest payments in either month. The limit of new short term credit is $ 900 000. This is a cumulative limit.

Possible new loan must be repaid in three months. The interest is payable in advance and is 12 percent per annum. The interest on new loans will be observed in the objective function and in the projected income statement only for a two month period if the loan is taken in May and for a one month period if it is taken in June.

Accrued income tax of the beginning balance must be paid in May. An income tax of 50 percent of the profit for each month is accrued in the projected balance sheets. However, this tax will not be paid before the end of June. No dividend payments take place in either month. Accrued wages remain roughly at the level of the beginning balance figure over the horizon.

The minimum cash balance for each month is $ 150 000. Any excess cash can be invested at an interest of 6 percent per annum. It should be noted that any deposit made can be withdrawn only after the horizon. If for example there is excess cash at the end of May the model must consider whether to invest them into the interest bearing account or to keep them in the firm in the form of free cash which does not earn any interest.

The subjective inventory carrying costs of seasonal inventories are 1 per cent per month. These are the storage and obsolescence costs which are additional to the costs of financing that are already taken into account via the cash constraint.

The following variables should be used in setting up the model:

$x_j(t)$ = sales of product j in period t, units of product,

$y_j(t)$ = production of product j in period t, units of product,

$z(t)$ = units of raw material purchased in period t,

$w(t)$ = loans taken in period t, $,

$v(t)$ = excess cash invested outside the firm in period t, $,

$u(t)$ = overtime in the mixing department in period t, hours,

$i_j(1)$ = seasonal inventory of product j in May, units of product,

$m(1)$ = free cash at the end of May, $ (= cash in excess of the minimum balance but not invested in an interest bearing account).

Required:
Develop the model, solve it and develop the budgets for the operations in May and June.

3-2. Assume that we are analyzing a two-period model. The length of the period is one month. The firm sells and makes two products, A and B. The sales in period t are denoted by x_{At} and x_{Bt}. The units produced are denoted by y_{At} and y_{Bt}. The sales and cost data is as follows:

	A	B
Sales price, $/unit	10.-	20.-
Terms of payment: in cash	20 %	–
in 30 days	30 %	50 %
in 60 days	40 %	50 %
Direct wages, $/unit	5.-	6.-
Raw material usage, unit/unit of product	4	12

Direct wages are paid in cash. Raw material is common for both products. The amount purchased in period t is denoted by z_t. The purchase price is $ 0.50/unit and the terms of payment net in 30 days. The raw material beginning balance is 10 000 units and the required minimum balance at the end of both months is 15 000 units.

The beginning cash balance is $ 3 000. The accounts receivable beginning balance is $ 12 000. One half of this balance is collected in the first period and the remainder in the second period. Fixed costs to be paid in cash are $ 8 000 in the first period and $ 9 000 in the second period. The loans existing at the beginning of the analysis must be amortized in the amount of $ 9 000 both in the first and in the second period. Dividends in the amount of $ 3 000 must be paid in the first period. The minimum cash balance is $ 4 000 at the end of the first period and $ 2 000 at the end of the second period. New loans can be taken in any desired amount but they must be paid back within one month and a 12 percent per annum interest must be paid on them together with the repayment. The taking of new loans in period t is denoted by v_t.

Required:
Develop a constraint for both periods requiring that the beginning balance plus cash receipts are equal to or exceed the cash expenditures plus the required minimum balance at the end of the period.

4 A Multi-Period Multi-Plant Model

The General Model Structure

The analysis has been extended step by step in the preceding chapters to cover a single period model of two plant as well as a two period model of a single plant. In the present chapter we will consider a two period two plant model. This will be the most extensive example of the present text. It will fall far short of the size of models needed in real firms. However, it will be large enough to demonstrate the essential features of such models.

The examples of chapters 2 and 3 will be used as a basis of the model to a degree possible. In the chapter about the two period model we already noted that the analogy to the single period two plant model is not complete and that the first period section of the model is tied to the second period section through the financial section of the model and not only through inventory variables (cf. Table 2-20 and 3-2). The example of the present chapter will be arranged in an order where the physical constraints of both periods come before the constraint for financing and net operating profit. This will demonstrate that as far as the physical operations are concerned the analogy is complete. The only exception is the fact that the transportation in time, i.e., carrying inventories, can only go in one direction whereas transportation between two locations can go into either direction.

Figure 9 shows the basic structure of the model. The rectangular at the top of the figure represents the coefficients of the objective function. The rectangular on the right hand side of the figure represents the right hand side coefficients of the constraints. Other sections of the figure represent various coefficients on the left hand side of the constraints. Beginning from the top, the first section of the constraints represent the first period sales, production, purchases, transportation, and inventories. Next in order are the respective second period constraints. The bottom section shows the financial constraints for both periods. Within each period the physical constraints have been organized in an order where the first set is for the parent plant and the second set for

107

the subsidiary plant.

The variables representing the transportation of goods between the plants in the first period are located between the parent and subsidiary plant variables. The variables representing seasonal inventories are again located between the first and second period variables. It is assumed in the model that both products can be transported between both factories and that both products can be stored in both plants.

The lower right hand section shows the financial variables (loans, interest, cash balance, net profit, and taxes) for both periods.

The Model in a Tabular Form

The model has been presented in the form of a table used for keypunching the input data in Table 4-1a, b, and c. Section a of the table shows all the variables of Figure 9 until the seasonal inventories of the parent plant at the end of the first period. Section b covers the variables from the seasonal inventories of the subsidiary plant at the end of the first period to the end of the subsidiary plant operations in the second period. Section c finally shows the remainder of Figure 9, i.e., the financial variables for both periods and the right hand side constants.

The variable names at the top of Table 4-1 have been combined from the variable names used in Tables 2-20 and 3-2. For example, x_{AP1} denotes the sales of product A in the parent plant in the first period, t_{APS2} the transportation of product A to the parent plant from the subsidiary in the second period, i_{BS1} the seasonal inventory of product B in the subsidiary plant at the end of the first period, etc.

In section c the variables v_1 and v_2 stand for the new loans taken, re_1 and re_2 for interest expenses, noe_1 and noe_2 for net operating earnings (since the income tax is 50 percent, they also stand for taxes), and the variables m_1 and m_2 for excess cash to be invested outside the firm at the rate of interest of 3 percent per period.

The row names are interpreted as follows. P at the beginning of the name stands for the parent plant and S for the subsidiary. The period is indicated by the figure at the end of the name. For example, PSALEA1 represents the parent plant sales of product A in the first period, SRAWMAW2 the subsidiary purchases of raw material W in the second period, etc.

The left hand side coefficients of the constraints have been taken out of the respective sections of Tables 2-20 and 3-2 except for some elements in the second period cash constraint (CASH2-row). These

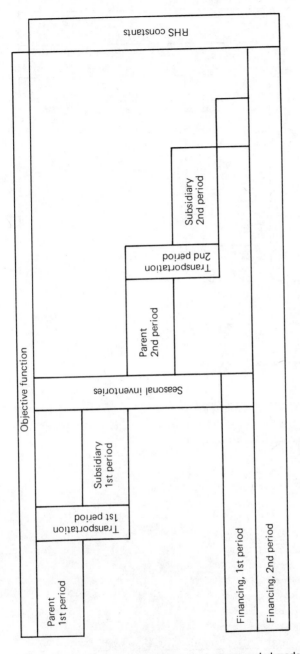

Figure 9. The basic structure of the two-plant two-period model.

	XAP1	XBP1	YAP1	YBP1	ZWP1	ZUP1	TAPS1	TASP1	TBPS1	TBSP1	XAS1	XBS1	YAS1	YBS1	ZWS1	ZUS1	IAP1	IBP1
CONTRIB	1.58	2.20	-1.4	-1.68	-0.14	-0.22	-.58	-.02	-.68	-.12	1.60	2.02	-1.68	-1.96	-0.14	-0.22	-.11	-.13
PSALEA1	1.						1.	-1.										
PSALEB1		1.							1.	-1.								
PINVENA1	-1.		1.														-1.	
PINVENB1		-1.		1.														-1.
PPRODCA1			0.5	0.6														
PRAWMAW1			-3.	-2.	1.													
PRAWMAU1						1.												
SSALEA1							-1.	1.			1.							
SSALEB1									-1.	1.		1.						
SINVENA1											-1.		1.					
SINVENB1												-1.		1.				
SPRODCA1													0.6	0.7				
SRAWMAW1													-3.	-2.	1.			
SRAWMAU1																1.		
PSALEA2																		
PSALEB2																		
PINVENA2																	1.	
PINVENB2																		1.
PPRODCA2																		
PRAWMAW2																		
PRAWMAU2																		
SSALEA2																		
SSALEB2																		
SINVENA2																		
SINVENB2																		
PPRODCA2																		
SRAWMAW2																		
SRAWMAU2																		
CASH1	3.15	4.28	-1.4	-1.68	-0.14	-0.22	-.3	-.3	-.4	-.4	3.42	4.57	-1.68	-1.96	-0.14	-0.22		
DEBTLIM1																		
INTREST1	1.58	2.20					-.58	-.02	-.68	-.12	1.60	2.02						
PROFIT1	0.28	0.13			-0.01	-0.015					0.31	0.14			-0.01	-0.015		
CASH2																		
DEBTLIM2																		
INTEREST2																		
PROFIT2																		

Table 4-1a A Two-Plant Two-Period Model

	IAS1	IBS1	XAP2	XBP2	YAP2	YBP2	ZWP2	ZUP2	TAPS2	TASP2	TBPS2	TBSP2	XAS2	XBS2	YAS2	YBS2	ZWS2	ZUS2
CONTRIB	-11	-18	1.52	2.20					-.58	-.02	-.68	-.12	1.60	2.02				
PSALEA1																		
PSALEB1																		
PINVENA1																		
PINVENB1																		
PPRODCA1																		
PRAWSMAW1		-1.																
PRAWMAU1																		
SSALEA1	-1.																	
SSALEB1																		
SINVENA1																		
SINVENB1																		
SPRODCA1																		
SRAWMAW1																		
SRAWMAU1																		
PSALEA2	1.		1.															
PSALEB2				1.														
PINVENA2			-1.		1.				1.	-1.								
PINVENB2				-1.		1.					1.	-1.						
PPRODCA2					0.5	0.6	1.											
PRAWMAW2					-3.	-2.												
PRAWMAU2								1.										
SSALEA2		1.											1.					
SSALEB2														1.				
SINVENA2									-1.	1.			-1.		1.			
SINVENB2											-1.	1.		-1.		1.		
SPRODCA2															0.6	0.7	1.	
SRAWMAW2															-3.	-2.		
SRAWMAU2																		1.
CASH1																		
DEBTLIM1																		
INTREST1																		
PROFIT1			3.15	4.28	-1.4	-1.68	-0.14	-0.22	-3.	-3.	-4	-4.	3.42	4.38	-1.68	-0.14	-0.22	
CASH2																		
DEBTLIM2																		
INTREST2																		
PROFIT2			1.58	2.20					-.58	-.02	-.68	-.12	1.60	2.02				

Table 4–1b. A Two-Plant Two-Period Model (Continued).

	V1	RE1	M1	NOE1	V2	RE2	M2	NOE2		RESTRIC
CONTRIB		-1.	0.03			-1.	0.03			
PSALEA1									≤	220 000.
PSALEB1									≤	300 000.
PINVENA1									≥	-5 000.
PINVENB1									≥	10 000.
PPRODCA1									≤	300 000.
PRAWMAW1									≥	10 000.
PRAWMAU1									≥	-10 000.
SSALEA1									≤	180 000.
SSALEB1									≤	150 000.
SINVENA1									≥	-2 000.
SINVENB1									≥	-1 500.
SPRODCA1									≤	220 000.
SRAWMAW1									≥	-2 000.
SRAWMAU1									≥	-3 000.
PSALEA2									≤	250 000.
PSALEB2									≤	300 000.
PINVENA2									≥	0.
PINVENB2									≥	0.
PPRODCA2									≤	280 000.
PRAWMAW2									≥	0.
PRAWMAU2									≥	0.
SSALEA2									≤	150 000.
SSALEB2									≤	200 000.
SINVENA2									≥	0.
SINVENB2									≥	0.
SPRODCA2									≤	230 000.
SRAWMAW2									≥	0.
SRAWMAU2									≥	0.
CASH1	1.		-1.						=	1 451 000.
DEBTLIM1	1.								≤	50 000.
INTREST1	-0.05	1.							=	5 000.
PROFIT1		-1.	0.03	-2.					=	1 465 000.
CASH2	-0.25		1.03	-1.	1.		-1.		=	1 229 500.
DEBTLIM2	0.8				1.				≤	100 000.
INTREST2	-0.04				-0.05	1.			=	4 500.
PROFIT2					-1.		0.03	-2.	=	1 465 000.

Table 4-1c. A Two-Plant Two-Period Model (Continued).

elements are related to the collection of the subsidiary plant sales that took place in the first period as well as to the payments for the first period purchases of raw materials made by the subsidiary. These coefficients have been derived in a manner analogous to the derivation of the respective coefficients for the parent plant.

The constraints for operating profit (PROFIT1- and PROFIT2-rows) include the costs of transporting goods between the plants. They also include the difference in standard costs for finished products transferred between the plants. When we take this cost difference into account at the time the products are moved from one plant to another we do not need to keep track of the goods in inventory and can use the profit contribution figures of each plant to compute the sales contribution without worrying about the origin of the goods. The unit contribution of the subsidiary sales is also included in these constraints.

Some changes have been made in the right-hand side coefficients of the constraints. The upper limits of sales and the available production capacity of the parent plant are at the levels of Table 3-2. The required minimum inventories are also at their previous levels. Instead, the upper limits of sales of the subsidiary plant have been changed. They are now assumed to be the following:

	1st Period	2nd Period
Product A	180 000 units	150 000 units
Product B	150 000 »	200 000 »

Table 4-2. The Demand for the Products of the Subsidiary Plant.

The production capacity of the subsidiary plants is 220 000 hours in the first period and 230 000 hours in the second period.

The constants on the right-hand side of the cash constraints have been obtained by adding to the respective constants in the single plant two period model the fixed cash expenses of the subsidiary plant given in Table 2-19. The constants on the right-hand side of the profit constraints are the sum of the fixed costs in the two plants.

Analysis of the Optimal Solution

The optimal solution of the model has been restated in an abbreviated form in Table 4-3. When we compare the values of the variables representing the sale of finished products to the upper limits of sales we note that only the sale of product A in the parent plant in the first period remains under the limit for the period. The optimal value of the variable x_{AP2} is 228 857 units while the respective upper limit is 250 000 units.

Both plants make product B in the first period in excess of minimum requirements: i_{BP1} = 10 833.33 units and i_{BS1} = 13 214.285 units. In the case of the parent plant the situation is the same as in the two period single plant model. The demand for product A shows the seasonality while the demand for product B remains stable. Yet the model chooses to make product B for seasonal inventory. An intuitive

Parent Plant		Subsidiary Plant	
Sales			
x_{AP1} = 220 000		x_{AS1} = 180 000	
x_{BP1} = 300 000		x_{BS1} = 150 000	
x_{AP2} = 228 857.145		x_{AS2} = 150 000	
x_{BP2} = 300 000		x_{BS2} = 200 000	
Inventories			
i_{AP1} = 0		i_{AS1} = 0	
i_{BP1} = 10 833.33		i_{BS1} = 13 214.285	
Transportation			
t_{APS1} = 0		t_{ASP1} = 0	
t_{BPS1} = 0		t_{BSP1} = 0	
t_{APS2} = 0		t_{ASP2} = 0	
t_{BPS2} = 13 214.285		t_{BSP2} = 0	
Production			
y_{AP1} = 215 000		y_{AS1} = 178 000	
y_{BP1} = 320 833.33		y_{BS1} = 161 714.286	
y_{AP2} = 228 857.145		y_{AS2} = 150 000	
y_{BP2} = 275 952.38		y_{BS2} = 199 999.999	
Raw Material Purchases			
z_{WP1} = 655 000		z_{WS1} = 532 000	
z_{UP1} = 631 666.67		z_{US1} = 320 428.573	
z_{WP2} = 686 571.436		z_{WS2} = 449 999.999	
z_{UP2} = 551 904.76		z_{US2} = 399 999.999	

Financing & Profit			
New Loans		Interest Expenses	
v_1 = 34 540.954		r_1 = 6 727.047	
v_2 = 0		r_2 = 5 881.638	
Excess Cash		Net Operating Profit	
m_1 = 0		noe_1 = 63 436.475	
m_2 = 411 189.225		noe_2 = 99 031.305	

Table 4-3. Optimal Program of the Two-Period Two-Plant Model.

solution would have been to carry in inventory the product with increasing demand.

Product transfer between the plants takes place in the second period. The seasonal inventory of product B in the subsidiary plant is being transferred to the parent plant in the second period: i_{BS1} = 13 214.285 units and t_{BPS2} = 13 214.285 units. The combined effect of the seasonal inventory in the subsidiary plant and the transfer of this inventory to the parent plant is to free production capacity in the parent plant to make a sufficient amount of product A in the second period.

The optimal values of the variables representing production agree with the seasonal inventory figures. The number of units of product A made in the parent plant in the second period equal the second period sales: y_{AP2} = 228 857 units. The available production capacity is used up in both periods. Raw material purchases follow production requirements.

The bottom section of Table 4-3 shows the values of the financial variables. The amount of new loans taken in the first period is $ 34 540.95. There are excess funds available at the end of the second period: m_2 = = 411 189.22.

The projected income statements drawn up on the basis of the optimal solution are shown in Tables 4-4 and 4-5. The income statement of the first period shown in Table 4-4 is analogous to the two plant single period statement of chapter 2. There are no transfers between plants and hence no transportation costs. There are no excess funds and therefore no interest income either. The subjective costs associated with the seasonal inventories i_{BP1} and i_{BS1} in the objective function are not reflected in the income statement.

The second period statement follows the same lines. Now there are some transportation costs due to the transfer of products between plants. The cost of transporting a unit of product B was assumed to be $ 0.40 per unit. The Total-column of the income statement also includes the difference between the standard costs of product B for the units transferred from plant S to plant P. The contribution of product B in the respective column of the parent plant has been computed by using the standard costs of the parent plant, $ 2.21 per unit. However, 13 214,285 units of these were made in the subsidiary plant at a standard cost of $ 2.49 per unit. The cost difference is (2.49 -2.21) 13 214.285 = $ 3 700.16. The interest income for the period has been computed by applying the rate of interest of 3 percent to the amount of excess cash, $ 411 189.

Other budgets are left as exercises to the reader.

Projected Income Statement 1st Period	Total	Parent			Subsidiary		
		Total	Product A	Product B	Total	Product A	Product B
Sales $	3 494 000	2 120 000	770 000	1 350 000	1 374 000	684 000	690 000
Less: Variable Selling Costs	68 500	42 400	15 400	27 000	26 100	12 600	13 500
Net Sales	3 425 500	2 077 600	754 600	1 323 000	1 347 900	671 400	676 500
Less: Standard Cost of Sales	1 826 900	1 070 000	407 000	663 000	756 900	383 400	373 500
Standard Contribution	1 598 600	1 007 600	347 600	660 000	591 000	288 000	303 000
Transportation Costs	—						
Production Cost Variances	—						
Contribution	1 598 600						
Interest Income	—						
Total	1 598 600						
Interest Expense	6 727,05						
	1 591 872.95						
Fixed Costs	1 465 000	915 000			550 000		
Income Tax	126 872.95						
Net Operating Profit	63 436.47						
Net Operating Profit	63 436.48						

Table 4–4. Projected income statement, 1st period.

116

Projected Income Statement 2nd Period	Total	Parent			Subsidiary		
		Total	Product A	Product B	Total	Product A	Product B
Sales, $	3 641 000	2 151 000	801 000	1 350 000	1 490 000	570 000	920 000
Less: Variable Selling Costs	71 520	43 020	16 020	27 000	27 000	10 500	18 000
Net Sales	3 469 480	2 007 980	784 980	1 323 000	1 461 500	559 500	902 000
Less: Standard Costs of Sales	1 903 885.72	1 086 385.72	423 285.72	663 000	817 500	319 500	498 000
Standard Contribution	1 665 594,67	1 021 594.28	361 594.28	660 000	644 000	240 000	404 000
Transportation Costs	5 285.94						
Production Cost Variances	3 700.16						
Contribution	1 656 608.57						
Interest Income	12 335.67						
Total	1 668 944.24						
Interest Expense	5 881.64						
	1 663 062.60						
Fixed Costs	1 465 000.00	915 000			550 000		
Income Tax	198 062.60						
Net Operating Profit	99 031.30						
	99 031.30						

Table 4-5. Projected income statement, 2nd period.

Problems

4-1. Develop the production-inventory and cash budgets on the basis of the solution given in Table 4-3.

4-2. Develop the projected balance sheets for both periods on the basis of the solution given in Table 4-3 and the projected income statements of Tables 4-4 and 4-5.

4-3. Assume that the terms of payment for the sale of product B imply that 85 percent of the sales revenue is collected during the sales period in both plants. In addition, assume that the firm can take new loans either in the first or in the second period to a total of $ 150 000 and that the repayments of the loan begin only after the horizon. Assume finally that the demand for product B in the first period in the parent plant is at most 280 000 units. Convert the problem presented in Table 4-1a, b, and c to conform with these assumptions, solve the new problem, and develop the respective budgets.

4-4. Reformulate problem 1-5 assuming that both plant K and plant L can carry both products in inventory. The inventory carrying costs are 25 percent of the manufacturing costs of the products. The upper limits of the sales of the two products are the following:

	Marketing Areas			
	N		S	
	Products		Products	
Upper limits of sales, units of product	A	B	A	B
1st period	8 000	12 000	7 000	7 000
2nd period	10 000	12 000	8 000	5 000

Other data for both periods is the same as given in problem 1-5. Write out the objective function and the constraints of the resulting two period problem.

4-5. Reformulate problem 1-5 as a two period problem. Assume that the changes introduced in problem 4-4 are still valid. In addition, assume that plant K serves sales area N and plant L sales area S. In other words, add to the model variables denoting transportation from plant K to plant L as well as transportation in the opposite direction and delete variables denoting products that go from plant K to area S and from plant L to area N. Assume that the cost of transporting products between plants is $ 0.50 per unit.

5 Optimization Models and the Control of Operations

The Principles of Control

To a large extend it is still true that mathematical programming and other formal models used for planning the operations of firms are designed and implemented by people in the area of production or in some other area of the firm which does not require any extensive knowledge of the theory underlying accounting concepts and practices. On the other hand, the same firms are still relying on the budgetary control process which is traditionally designed and implemented by accountants. Traditional accounting curriculum has not paid much attention to optimization techniques. It follows that the co-operation between model builders and budget people has often been less than perfect.

The main theme of the present text has been that budgetary process should be based on the use of optimization models. In order to secure a one-to-one correspondence between the optimal solutions of formal planning models and the budgets it is necessary that these models are tightly built into the accounting model of the firm. To accomplish this it is necessary to have people who understand both the possibilities offered by formal models and the theory underlying budgeting and standard cost systems. So far we have analyzed the connections between models and budgets. We now turn to the control aspect of the management process.

Planning and control of the operations of a firm form a loop in which the plan is followed by operations and operations are followed by measurement of the actual results. In the next step the plan and the actual results are compared and the variance, i.e., the difference between the plan and the actual results is computed. If there is no significant difference, operations must have proceeded in accordance with the plan and there is no need for management action. On the other hand, if there is a significant variance, we must find the reason for it. It is possible that operations have been carried out in a less than ideal way. It is also possible that the plan itself is at fault. If operations are out of line corrective measures must be taken if this is still feasible. If the plans have not been in order the planning system should learn from the mistakes so that they are not repeated in the next planning cycle.

A traditional way to compare operations to plans has been to use the variance analysis of standard cost systems. When the work has proceeded along the lines indicated above it has become increasingly evident that internal accounting techniques are in the need of a revision if the full potential of the new planning techniques is to be realized. It is the purpose of the present chapter to present a few simple examples indicating possible ways to extend the control technique with the help of an optimization model.

The application of the traditional control technique to situations where a formal optimization model was used as a basis of the budget has two shortcomings.[1] First, it often leaves a number of data inputs to the decision model outside the analysis, i.e. it does not make a full utilization of information provided by formal models. Secondly, and even more importantly, the traditional analysis tends to proceed with a ceteris paribus-assumption when a mutatis mutandis-assumption would be appropriate. In other words, the traditional analysis ignores the decision alterations implied by many of the deviations encountered.

In the approach suggested by Demski the firm is viewed as periodically resolving its planning model on the basis of re-estimated data inputs. The program produced by the solution of the model at the planning stats is called the ex ante program. This program forms the basis of the budget for the coming period and is subsequently implemented. Whereas the traditional accounting analysis observes the actual results obtained and compares these with the ex ante program, the system proposed by Demski carries this traditional analysis one step further. This is achieved by the preparation of an "after-the-fact" budget which indicates optimal performance in terms of information available at the end of the period. This is the program the firm would have used if it had had a perfect foresight at the beginning of the period covered by the budget. It is called the ex post optimum program.

Instead of comparing the observed actual results with the ex ante program the firm should use all three sets of data: the ex ante, ex post and actual observed data.

"The difference between ex ante and ex post results is a crude measure of the firm´s forecasting ability. It is the difference between what the firm planned to do during the particular period and what it

---

1 Demski, Joel S., "An Accounting System Structured on a Linear Programming Model", The Accounting Review, (October, 1967), pp. 701-712.

should have planned to do. Similarly, the difference between ex post and observed is the difference between what the firm should have accomplished during the period and what it actually did accomplish. It is the opportunity cost to the firm of not using its fixed facilities to maximum advantage."[2]

If we use the following notation:

Traditional Variance = Ex Ante Budget - Actual Observed Program,
Planning Variance = Ex Ante Budget - Ex Post Optimum Program,
and
Ex Post Variance = Ex Post Optimum Program
                   - Actual Observed Program,

then we can see that the relationsjip between the traditional variance and the two variances proposed by Demski is given by the following equation:

Traditional Variance = Planning Variance + Ex Post Variance.

In Demski's procedure the ex post variance is attributed to the management and would disappear completely if the management adapted its operations optimally to the changing circumstances. The implication of this approach is that the middle management is encouraged to depart from the original budget whenever it deems that such a departure is to the firm's advantage. On the other hand, one of the main objectives of the budget is to ensure the co-ordination of operations throughout the organixation. If every middle manager begins to modify his operations to what he believes to be the best for the company then the whole budgeting process is in danger of losing its significance and it is very probable that the actions of individual middle managers are no longer consistent with each other. It seems possible that more harm can result from the disregard of budgets than from the execution of a budget which is no longer optimal but is throughout consistent.

If we accept this view, then it is still worth while to compute the traditional variance. Demski's approach and the traditional variance analysis can be reconciled when we observe that

Ex Post Variance = Traditional Variance - Planning Variance.

Furthermore, this order of computing the variances allows us to extend the use of ex post data. We know that the traditional variance can be divided into a component which represents unavoidable deviations

---

2 Demski, op. cit., p. 702.

from the budget and the avoidable component. An unavoidable component may result, for example, from a fall in the sales price of the product. Since the new and lower sales price which was forced on the firm by the market is necessarily included in the data for the ex post program, we might as well use it in the analysis of the traditional variance. We can decompose the traditional variance into a component which was unavoidable and into a component which may have been avoidable and which needs closer analysis.

Traditional Analysis

It is not possible to cover exhaustively the traditional standard cost variance analysis in the present text. Instead, we will present two short examples. The first example is the firm in chapter 1. Let us assume that the sales price and the contribution margin of product A fall during the budget period for reasons beyond the control of the management. The actual sales price is $ 550 per unit of product. The firm follows the original budget by making and selling 6 units of product A and 3 units of product B which is the optimal solution of Figure 3. The traditional variance analysis would begin by comparing the budget and the actual data:

Product	Qty	Budget Price $/unit	Total $	Std. Contribution $/unit	Qty	Actual Price $/unit	Total $
A	6	900	5 400	600	6	550	3 300
B	3	800	2 400	200	3	800	2 400
			7 800				5 700

Table 5-1. Marketing Data

These data are used to compute the difference in the total contribution between the budget and the actual and analyze how much of this difference is due to changes in prices and how much due to changes in quantities (in the present text we will consider only price and quantity variance). The amount to be analyzed is the standard contribution (= sales price – standard cost), since we are now analyzing marketing variances and since the production departments are held responsible for making the products at standard costs. Marketing is held responsible for selling the budgeted amounts of products and selling them at prices which bring the budgeted contribution.

The price variance is the difference between the actual and the standard price multiplied by the actual quantity. The standard price is the price used in the original budget.

Product	Actual Price	Standard Price	Actual Quantity	Price Variance, $
A	550	900	6	−2100 Unfavorable
B	800	800	3	0
Total Price Variance				−2100 Unfavorable

Table 5-2. Traditional Price Variance.

The price variance in the present example is unfavorable because it reduces the total contribution from the figure in the original budget.

The quantity variance is the difference between the quantity actually sold and the standard quantity multiplied by the standard contribution per unit. The standard quantity is the quantity in the ex ante budget. The standard contribution is the sales price in the budget less standard costs.

Product	Standard Contribution	Actual Quantity	Standard Quantity	Quantity Variance, $
A	600	6	6	0
B	200	3	3	0
Total Quantity Variance				

Table 5-3. Traditional Quantity Variance.

According to the traditional variance analysis, the firm has lost $ 2 100 due to unfavorable price variance. There is no quantity variance in the present example.

As a second example of the traditional variance analysis we will consider a firm which is preparing a budget under the assumptions of chapter 1 except for the upper limit of sales of product A which is now assumed to be 9 units of product. The model for the ex ante budget has an objective function given by (1-1) and constraints given by (1-2) to (1-5) except for the constraint

$$x_1 \leq 9$$

which is now the upper limit of sales of product A.

By checking Figure 3 it can be seen that now the optimal program is given by the intersection of the cash constraint and the x_1-axis:

$$x_1' = 8, \quad x_2' = 0, \text{ and } Z' = 600(8) + 200(0) = \$ 4\ 800.$$

Assume that the firm has developed the budgets on the basis of this solution and carried out these budgets exactly. The production and sales of product A are 8 units. The sales price has been $ 900 per unit as budgeted. Assume now that during the budget period there is a general increase in the market price of product B. The new price is $ 1 250 per unit. The traditional variance analysis now gives the following results:

Product A	Actual Price 900	Standard Price 900	Actual Quantity 8	Variance 0
Total Price Variance				0
Product	Standard Contribution	Actual Quantity	Standard Quantity	Variance
A	600	8	8	0
Total Quantity Variance				0

Table 5–4. Traditional Variance Analysis of the Second Example.

In this second example the traditional analysis gives results which indicate that operations have followed plans and there is no reason for changes in operations.

Ex Post Budget and Variance Analysis

We next consider the same examples in the light of an ex post budget and carry out Demski´s variance analysis. The ex post budget of the first example is derived by solving a problem where the model is based on data available at the end of the budget period. These data give rise to the following model:

Maximize $Z = 250x_1 + 200x_2$

subject to

$$x_1 \leq 6$$
$$x_2 \leq 10$$
$$10x_1 + 20x_2 \leq 160$$
$$300x_1 + 200x_2 \leq 2\ 400$$

and

$$x_1 \geq 0,\ x_2 \geq 0.$$

A graphic solution to this model has been presented in Figure 10. Point B gives the optimal program which is 4 units of product A and 6 units of product B. The optimal contribution is $ 2 200.

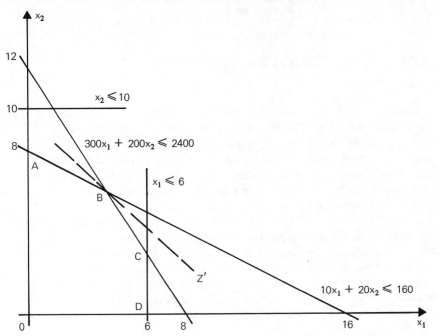

Figure 10. Optimal program of the ex post budget in the first example.

We next compute the planning variance which is the difference between the ex ante budget and the ex post budget:

Product	Ex Ante Budget			Ex Post Budget			Planning Variance $
	Contribution	Quantity	Total $	Contribution	Quantity	Total $	
A	600	6	3 600	250	4	1 000	2 600
B	200	3	600	200	6	1 200	−600
			4 200			2 200	2 000

Table 5-5. The Planning Variance of the First Example.

The planning variance shows that the firm´s ex ante budget was too optimistic. Because the firm did not anticipate the future price development the total contribution of the ex ante budget is $ 2 000 in excess of what it should have been.

The ex post variance is the difference between the ex post budget and the actual program:

125

Product	Ex Post Budget Contribution	Quantity	Total $	Actual Program Contribution	Quantity	Total $	Ex Posts Variance $
A	250	4	1 000	250	6	1 500	−500
B	200	6	1 200	200	3	600	600
			2 200			2 100	100

Table 5-6. The Ex Post Variance of the First Example.

The ex post variance shows that the firm has lost $ 100 in addition to the planning variance. The ex post variance is a result of nonoptimal use of resources in changed circumstances. The total contribution of the firm would have been $ 100 larger if it had been able to react to changed circumstances in an optimal way, i.e. if it could have switched to the ex post budget immediatelly after the change in the sales price instead of following the ex ante program.

The total variance of Table 5-2 was $ 2 100. This is also the sum of the planning and ex post variance. However, the traditional variance does not reveal that the firm could have avoided $ 100 of this total if it could have reacted without delay to changed circumstances.

We next turn to the ex post budget of the second example of the preceding section. We must now solve the following model:

Maximize $Z = 600 x_1 + 650x_2$

subject to

$$x_1 \leq 9$$
$$x_2 \leq 10$$
$$10x_1 + 20x_2 \leq 160$$
$$300x_1 - 25x_2 \leq 2\,400$$

and

$$x_1 \geq 0, \ x_2 \geq 0.$$

The change in the cash constraint is also a result of the change in the sales price of product B. Cash collections from the sale of product B were assumed to be 50 per cent. If the price of product B is increased to $ 1 250 per unit the production and sale of one unit of product will bring a cash inflow of (0.5)1 250 - 600 = $ 25 per unit.

Figure 11 gives the solution of the ex post budget model. It can be seen that 8.32 units of product A and 3.84 units of product B are made and sold in the optimal solution. Using these figures we can again compute the planning and ex post variances for the second example.

126

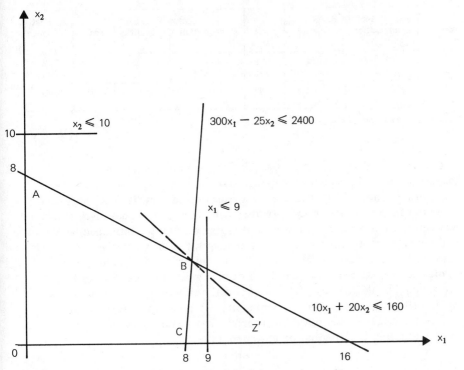

Figure II. Optimal solution of the ex post budget of the second example.

Product	Ex Ante Budget Contribution	Quantity	Total $	Ex Post Budget Contribution	Quantity	Total $	Planning Variance $
A	600	8	4 800	600	8.32	4 992	− 192
B	200	0	—	650	3.84	2 496	−2 496
			4 800			7 488	−2 688

Table 5-7. The Planning Variance of the Second Example.

    The planning variance of the second example shows that the total contribution of the ex ante budget is $ 2 688 smaller than what would have been possible if the firm had a perfect foresight. While the planning variance of the first example showed that the ex ante budget was too optimistic the corresponding variance of the second example indicates that now the ex ante budget has been too pessimistic.

    The ex post variance of Table 5-8 shows that the firm has lost the amount of the total planning variance because it followed the original ex

Product	Ex Post Budget Contribution	Quantity	Total $	Actual Program Contribution	Quantity	Total $	Ex Post Variance $
A	600	8.32	4 992	600	8	4 800	192
B	650	3.84	2 496	650	0	–	2 496
			7 488			4 800	2 688

Table 5-8. The Ex Post Variance of the Second Example.

ante budget without modifications. The opportunity costs due to nonoptimal use of production capacity are $ 2 688.

It can be concluded that in the first example the traditional analysis indicated the existence of the variance although it could not distinguish between the variance due to forecasting errors and the variance which could have been avoided by immediate adaptation of operations to changes in the environment. However, in the second example the traditional variance analysis did not even signal the existence of the variance. The deficiency of the traditional analysis is that is does not measure the cost of foregone opportunity. It does not observe and evaluate changes in the optimal program that result from changes in data underlying the original ex ante program.

Reconciliation of Traditional and Ex Post Analysis

The planning and ex post variances computed with the help of the ex post budget do not directly indicate the deviation of the actual observed program from the original budget. If the basic principle of the budgeting system is that budget should be followed to ensure the consistency of operations even in the case where the budget is no longer optimal at the time of operations, then it follows that the traditional analysis still has a useful role to play. It shows the deviations of the actual program from the budget. On the other hand, the knowledge of the planning variance is also useful. If the planning variance tends to be large the firm should reconsider its forecasting methods.

Traditional analysis and Demski's ex post analysis can be reconciled when we take into account the following relationship between the variances:

Ex Post Variance = Traditional Variance – Planning Variance.

In other words, we compute the traditional variance and the planning variance with a minus sign. If we need the ex post variance we get it by deducting the rearranged planning variance from the traditional variance.

In addition, we can now decompose the traditional variance into new components. Instead of computing the normal price and quantity variances of which we do not know without any further analysis whether they are a result of mismanagement or changes in the environmental factors about which the management does not have any influence, we can decompose the traditional variance into an unavoidable component and a component which may have been avoidable. This order of computing the variances saves the management´s time. The management can concentrate on the component which represents a variance which might have been avoided.

Let us review the examples presented in the preceding sections in the light of this reasoning and carry out the analysis in the order just indicated.

The variances that could not have been avoided if the ex ante budget was followed are a result of changes either in prices or in sales quantities. These changes can be determined by comparing the models for ex ante and ex post budgets. If there is an unfavorable change in the sales price (and, therefore, in the contribution margin) of a product which is beyond the management´s control, this change can be determined by comparing the sales prices in the two models. If a price is reduced in the ex post model from what it was in the ex ante model it is by definition due to factors beyond the management´s control. This is because the price reductions initiated by the management would not be considered in the ex post model.

Let us review the price data of the first example and register the price reductions which fit this definition:

Product	Prices in Ex Post Model	Prices in Ex Ante Model	Unfavorable Price Difference $/unit
A	550	900	−350
B	800	800	0

Table 5-9. Unfavorable unavoidable price differences.

In an analogous way we must analyze the upper limits of sales in the ex post model and the sales quantities in the optimal program of the ex ante model. If the upper limit of sales in the ex post model is lower than the value of the respective variable in the optimal program of the ex ante model then there is an unfavorable unavoidable quantity difference. This difference is again by definition outside the management´s control. Ex post models do not include upper limits of sales which have been reduced from the ex ante levels by deliberate management action.

Product	Upper Limits of Ex Post Model	Optimal Program of Ex Ante Model	Unfavorable Difference in Quantity	Ex Ante Program less Unfavorable Difference
A	6	6	0	6
B	10	3	0	3

Table 5-10. Unfavorable unavoidable quantity differences of the first example.

If the upper limit of the ex post program is larger than the value of the respective variable in the optimal ex ante program there is no unfavorable quantity difference that could not have been avoided. For example, the element on the row of product B in the column giving the unfavorable difference in quantity is zero.

By using the right-hand side columns of Tables 5-9 and 5-10 we can factor the traditional variances computed in Tables 5-2 and 5-3 into two components:

Product	Unfavorable Price Difference	Ex Ante Program less Unfavorable Qty Difference	Price Variance	Other Price Variances $	Total Price Variances $
A	−350	6	−2 100	0	−2 100
B	0	3	0	0	0
			−2 100	0	−2 100

Table 5-11. Factoring of the Traditional Price Variance.

Product	Unfavorable Unavoidable Quantity Variance			Other Quantity Variances $	Total Quantity Variances $
	Standard Contribution $/unit	Unfavorable Difference in Quantity	Quantity Variance $		
A	600	0	0	0	0
B	200	0	0	0	0
			0	0	0

Table 5-12. Factoring of the Traditional Quantity Variance.

130

Table 5-11 shows that the total price variance is unavoidable if the firm wishes to follow the original budget. Since the total quantity variance is zero there is no unavoidable component, either.

In order to compute the total ex post variance we deduct the planning variance from the traditional variance:

Ex Post Variance = 2 100 - 2 000 = 100.

There is no unavoidable price and quantity variance in the second example, since there is no traditional variance. Therefore, it is not necessary to carry out the analysis of Tables 5-11 and 5-12 with respect to the second example. The total ex post variance could again be computed as a difference between the traditional and planning variance:

Ex Post Variance = 0 - (-2 688) = 2 688.

The analysis of the present chapter has been limited to marketing variances. Ex post analysis could also be extended to production variances. If the prices and supply conditions of raw materials change, and if some materials can be replaced by others, and particularly if the raw material requirements can be represented in the form of upper or lower limits, the standard uses of raw materials are no longer given in advance. Instead, they form a part of the problem to be solved and we can then talk about optimal standards. When prices and supply conditions of raw materials change, there may be changes in the optimal use of raw materials when we move from ex ante to ex post budget. We can then extend the ex post analysis to production variances to develop the respective planning and ex post variances.

6 Goal Programming and the Analysis of Conflicting Goals

Goal Programming Fundamentals[1]

Let us consider the example of chapter 1 which introduced linear programming. Assume that the loans in the beginning balance are short term loans to be deducted from working capital. It follows that the beginning balance of the working capital is $ 2 900:

Current Assets	$ 13 800
Less: Current Liabilities	10 900
Working Capital	$ 2 900

The firm is carrying out its planning in a situation where strategic decisions must be taken into account in the annual budget. The management wants to expand the operations and intends to raise additional capital by issuing new shares in the year following the budget period. To guarantee the success of the new issue the financial statements of the budget year should present the best possible picture of the firm to the prospective investors. The projected income for the year should be at a satisfactory level. The projected balance sheet should also show a healthy development. For our present purposes a healthy balance sheet is a balance sheet with working capital at least at a given level. In other words, the management now has two goals, income and working capital, and it attempts to achieve both of these goals simultaneously.

A satisfactory income for the firm is defined by the management as a return of 20 percent on equity. The equity in the beginning balance is $ 7 400. We disregard the corporate income tax in the present example. We can then say that the income goal is $ 1 500. According to the data of chapter 1, the fixed overhead budget is $ 3 200. In order to achieve its income goal the firm should make sales which bring a total contribution of 1 500 + 3 200 = $ 4 700. If we do not reach this goal there will be a negative deviation of actual contribution from the goal. On the

---

1 Goal Programming was originally formulated by Charnes and Cooper. See Charnes, A. and Cooper, W.W., <u>Management Models and Industrial Applications of Linear Programming,</u> Vol. 1 & 2 (New York: Wiley, 1961). See also Ijiri, Yuji, <u>Management Goals and Accounting for Control</u> (Amsterdam: North-Holland, 1965).

other hand, if we sell more than enough to reach this goal there will be a positive deviation of actual contribution from the goal. The overshooting of the goal in this example is not harmful. However, we will later consider examples where we try to avoid both the negative and the positive deviations from the goals.

The equation

$$\text{Actual Contribution} \overset{+}{-} \text{Deviations} = \text{Goal}$$

can be written as

$$600\ x_1 + 200x_2 + y^- - y^+ = 4\ 700$$

in the present example. The total contribution is the unit contribution times the number of units sold summed over all products: $600x_1 + 200x_2$. Variable y^- denotes the negative deviation from the goal of \$ 4 700. Variable y^+ shows again the positive deviation from this goal.

Assume first that variable y^+ equals zero and consider the feasible values of variable y^-. When the sales of the products in the product mix increase from zero the value of y^- decreases. Suppose, for example, that $x_1 = x_2 = 1$. Then

$$600(1) + 200(1) + y^- = 4\ 700$$

from which we get

$$y^- = 4\ 700 - 800 = 3\ 900.$$

Suppose next that $x_1 = x_2 = 2$. Then

$$600(2) + 200(2) + y^- = 4\ 700$$
or $$y^- = 3\ 100.$$

Looking at the same set of figures in a contrary way we can say that by reducing the value of variable y^- and by maintaining the equality we push the values of x_1 and/or x_2 upwards. The smaller the value of y^- becomes the larger is the value of the contribution and the closer is the left-hand side of the equation to the goal on the right-hand side. When $y^- = 0$ the values of variables x_1 and x_2 will be such that the goal is exactly reached.

Let us next consider a situation where $y^- = 0$ and y^+ increases. The more y^+ increases the larger must the total contribution get for the equation to hold. On the other hand, if we have a problem where the overachievement of a goal is inadvisable we get closer to the goal by reducing the value of y^+. When both $y^- = 0$ and $y^+ = 0$, we have reached the goal exactly. The Simplex method of linear programming automatically ensures that both of the deviational variables are not at nonzero levels at the same time, i.e. if $y^- > 0$, then $y^+ = 0$ and contrarywise.

We assumed that the second goal of the management is to get the working capital to a given level. Assume now that this level is \$ 3 000. We now have two conflicting goals. We can increase the working capital by increasing the cash funds or the inventory of finished goods. However, the funds in the form of idle cash and the goods in the form of unsold inventories will not increase profits. It can be seen that the working capital goal is in conflict with the profit goal.

This is a common situation in the case of several goals. There are alternative ways to analyze conflicting goals. One possibility is to treat all other goals as constraints and optimize with respect to the last goal. This is also the approach taken in the present example. We formulate the working capital goal as a constraint and optimize with respect to the contribution subject to the working capital constraint as well as other constraints of the problem given in chapter 1.

In order to prepare for later development we will slightly alter the example of chapter 1, however, with respect to the fixed cash receipts and expenses. We now assume that fixed cash receipts include new short term loans in the amount of \$ 1 200. The fixed cash expenses include a dividend payment in the amount of \$ 700 and also a capital expenditure of \$ 500. The new cash receipts equal the additions to the fixed cash expenses. Therefore, the balance remaining for the financing of the operations is still \$ 2 400 as in the original example:

Funds Available		
Beginning Cash Balance	\$ 1 000	
Accounts Receivable Balance	6 800	
New Short-Term Loans	1 200	9 000
Less: Fixed Cash Expenses		
Accounts Payable Balance	900	
Repayment of Loans	2 100	
Fixed Overhead	1 900	
Dividends	700	
Capital Budget	500	6 100
Subtotal		2 900
Less: Required Ending Balance		500
Cash Available for Financing the Operations		\$ 2 400

It was observed that the beginning balance of working capital is \$ 2 900. The ending balance is by definition the beginning balance plus increases less decreases. We must now list all the possible increases and decreases.

Let us first consider the increases and decreases in the framework of T-accounts familiar to accounting students. The entries to working capital are accounting entries that are made to cash, accounts receivable, inventories, accounts payable, or short term loans. All these accounts are lumped into one account called working capital. Other possible accounts of the present example are income, equity and fixed assets. Figure 12 shows the effects of all possible entries on the working capital.

In the present example the working capital is increased by the sales of the products. The debit is to accounts receivable and the credit to the income statement. The working capital is decreased by the cost of goods sold and the fixed costs less depreciation. The dividends as well as the capital expenditures reduce working capital.

The normal way to present changes in working capital in accounting textbooks is to say that working capital is increased by depreciation and net profit. The depreciation is added to the debit of the income account in Figure 12 to show that the effect of the net income and the depreciation has already been taken into account by the first three items, i.e., sales, variable costs and fixed costs. If the income tax is disregarded, the net effect of these three items will be equal to the sum of depreciation and net profit.

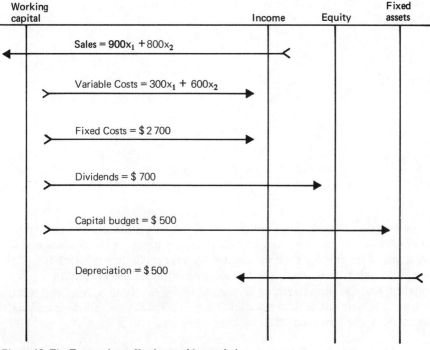

Figure 12. The Transactions affecting working capital

The collection of accounts receivable, the payment of accounts payable, the repayment of short-term loans, and the taking of new loans are transactions which do not affect the amount of working capital. If the loans in the example were long term loans, the taking and repayments of these loans would, of course, affect the balance of working capital.

Following the graphic representation of the changes in working capital in Figure 12 we can write the constraint which requires that the ending balance of working capital must meet the management goals:

$$2\,900 + 900x_1 + 800x_2 - 300x_1 - 600x_2 - 2\,700 - 700 - 500 \geq 3\,000.$$

This can be reduced to

$$600x_1 + 200x_2 \geq 4\,000.$$

Our problem is now to minimize the unfavorable deviation from the contribution goal, and if we succeed in this, maximize the favorable deviation from the goal subject to the constraints developed in chapter 1 and above:

(6-1)   Minimize Z = $y^- + y^+$
subject to

$$
\begin{aligned}
x_1 &\leq 6 \\
x_2 &\leq 10 \\
10x_1 + 20x_2 &\leq 160 \\
300x_1 + 200x_2 &\leq 2\,400 \\
600x_1 + 200x_2 &\geq 4\,000 \\
600x_1 + 200x_2 + y^- - y^+ &= 4\,700
\end{aligned}
$$

(6-2)

and

$$x_1,\ x_2,\ y^-,\ y^+ \geq 0.$$

The function to be minimized is $y^- - y^+$. It was stated above that in the present example, we wish to minimize the unfavorable deviation and if this is possible, then maximize the favorable deviation. The apparent contradiction between the maximization of the favorable deviation and the minimization of the objective function is resolved when we take into account that to maximize a given function y^+ is the same as to minimize the same function multiplied by -1, i.e.,

Minimize $-y^+$ = Maximize y^+.

It should be emphasized that objective function of the present example is a special case where we wish to overexceed the goal of the total contribution. If we wanted to achieve the goal exactly we would write the objective function as follows:

$$\text{Min } Z = y^- + y^+.$$

When the contribution goal is now approached from below we will never overshoot the goal because the value of variable y^- cannot be reduced below zero due to the nonnegativity constraint. When $y^- = 0$ and $y^+ = 0$, the value of the function to be minimized would also be zero.

The problem can be solved as a normal linear programming problem. The optimal solution is

$$x_1 = 6, \qquad y^- = 500,$$
$$x_2 = 3, \qquad y^+ = \quad 0.$$

Since there is a negative deviation from the profit goal, it cannot be reached completely. The problem could also be solved as an ordinary linear programming problem where the objective function is given by (1-1) and the constraints are (1-2) to (1-4) plus the working capital constraint developed in the present section. If we draw the working capital constraint in Figure 3 it can be seen that it goes between the origin and point C. The optimal solution of Figure 3 would not change. The optimal contribution would remain at the level of $ 4 200. This is equivalent to the result reached above: $ 4 200 + $ 500 = $ 4 700.

Analysis of Conflicting Goals

In the preceding section we assumed the working capital goal to be so important that it had to be met in the form of an inequality. The goal was formulated as a constraint limiting the solution space. The example was built on purpose in such a way that it did not work against the achievement of the other objective, the maximization of the contribution. This can be checked by drawing the working capital constraint in Figure 3. The optimal point is not disturbed.

The preceding example is clearly a special case. Not all goals have the priority given to the working capital goal. If the goal cannot be reached completely, we will allow a deviation from it. Following this line of thought we might say that we will allow a deviation from the working capital goal if it leads to a better achievement of the goal on contribution.

Often the management has more than two goals which are in mutual conflict like the goals in the preceding example. In order to keep with the simplest possible example to demonstrate the analysis of three goals we assume that the firm of chapter 1 tries to achieve given levels of contribution, working capital and cash. If these goals cannot be completely met we allow deviation from any of them.

We assume that the management has ordered the goals according to their importance. The most important goal is the contribution. The negative deviation from the contribution goal should be avoided. This goal can be overachieved but the firm is not actively striving for overachievement. The working capital goal is the second in the order of importance. This goal can also be overachieved although we do not actively strive for it. The least important goal is the level of cash balance. Instead of setting up the liquidity constraint in the form of an inequality which requires that a minimum cash balance be maintained we convert the minimum cash balance into a goal from which the program can deviate if more important goals so require.

Overachievement of the cash balance goal is permitted but not actively sought. On the other hand, we must observe the requirement that the cash balance cannot be negative. We must therefore set an upper limit to the negative deviation from the cash balance goal.

In order to write out the problem we use subscripts to identify the deviations y^- and y^+. The contribution goal can now be written as

$$600x_1 + 200x_2 + y_1^- - y_1^+ = 4\ 700.$$

The working capital goal can now be over- or underachieved. We must therefore join variables y_2^- and y_2^+ to the respective constraint:

$$2\ 900 + 900x_1 + 800x_2 - 300x_1 - 600x_2 - 2\ 700 - 700 - 500 + y_2^- - y_2^+ = 3\ 000$$

This can be reduced to

$$600x_1 + 200x_2 + y_2^- - y_2^+ = 4\ 000.$$

To develop the cash balance goal we take the beginning balance and add to it all cash receipts and deduct from it all cash expenses. The resulting closing balance toghether with the deviations is then set equal to the target closing balance:

$$1\ 000 + 6\ 800 + 1\ 200 - 900 - 2\ 100 - 1\ 900 - 700 - 500 + (0)900x_1 + (0.5)800x_2 - 300x_1 - 600x_2 + y_3^- - y_3^+ = 500.$$

This equation reduces to

$$- 300x_1 - 200x_2 + y_3^- - y_3^+ = -2\,400.$$

Multiplying by -1 we get

$$300x_1 + 200x_2 - y_3^- + y_3^+ = 2\,400.$$

Due to the figures in this particular example we now have the negative deviation y_3^- with a minus sign and the positive deviation y_3^+ with a plus sign. The interpretation is still the same: the actual balance plus the negative less the positive deviation equals the goal.

The actual closing cash balance cannot be negative. We must therefore set an upper limit to the negative deviation:

$$y_3^- \le 500.$$

We now have three goals which we try to achieve in a given order of priority. To indicate this order we associate with the deviational variables priority factors M_j where $j = 1$ stands for the least important goal, $j = 2$ the next goal, etc. Since we have three levels of goals the highest index of the priority factors is $J = 3$. The problem is now

(6-3) $\text{Min } Z = M_3 y_1^- + M_2 y_2^- + M_1 y_3^-$

subject to

(6-4)

$$
\begin{aligned}
x_1 & & & & & & \le & 6 \\
& x_2 & & & & & \le & 10 \\
10x_1 &+ 20x_2 & & & & & \le & 160 \\
300x_1 &+ 200x_2 & & & - y_3^- + y_3^+ & = & 2\,400 \\
600x_1 &+ 200x_2 & & + y_2^- - y_2^+ & & = & 4\,000 \\
600x_1 &+ 200x_2 &+ y_1^- - y_1^+ & & & = & 4\,700 \\
& & & & y_3^- & \le & 500
\end{aligned}
$$

and

$$x_1, x_2, y_1^-, y_1^+, y_2^-, y_2^+, y_3^-, y_3^+ \ge 0.$$

The objective function of goal programming is minimized by beginning with the variable(s) in the highest priority group. The value of the variable(s) is brought down regardless of what happens to the other variables in the objective function. This is achieved by assuming that the relationship between the priority factors can be represented as

$$M_3 \ggg M_2 \ggg M_1,$$

where the sign $\ggg$ indicates that the priority factor M_{j+1} is always larger than M_j multiplied by the real number n no matter how large we make n.

The minimization under pre-emptive order of priorities requires a slight change in the Simplex procedure. Since we have not covered the Simplex method in the present text we cannot go into the required changes, either. At this point we refer to the classical textbooks on the subject.[1] The example is solved by using the normal Simplex routine where we replace the pre-emptive priorities by real numbers +1 000 000,. +1 000, and +1. The objective function therefore becomes

$$\text{Min } Z = 1\ 000\ 000 y_1^- + 1\ 000 y_2^- + y_3^-.$$

The optimal program of this problem can be read in Table 6-1:

$$x_1 = 6,\ y_1^- = 100,\ y_2^- = 0,\ y_3^- = 400,$$
$$x_2 = 5,\ y_1^+ = 0,\ y_2^+ = 600,\ y_3^+ = 0.$$

The most important goal, i.e., the contribution of $ 4 700 cannot be reached completely. There is a negative deviation of $ 100. This is shown by the optimal value of variable y_1^-. The same conclusion can of course be reached by checking the optimal values of x_1 and x_2:

$$ 4\ 700 - $ 600(6) + 200(5) = 100.$$

It is interesting to note that the second goal is reached completely. The optimal value of the variable representing the negative deviation is zero: $y_2^- = 0$. In fact, this goal is overachieved by $ 600: $y_2^+ = 600$. The variable representing the positive deviation is not in the objective function and the solution process does not attempt to minimize it. The overachievement of the working capital goal can also be checked by preparing the projected financial statements. These have been presented in Tables 6-2 to 6-4.

---

1 Charnes, A, and W. W. Cooper, Management Models and Industrial Applications of Linear Programming, Vol. 1 & 2 (New York: Wiley, 1961), Ijiri, Y., Management Goals and Accounting for Control Amsterdam: North Holland, 1965).

	X1	X2	Y-1	Y+1	Y-2	Y+2	Y-3	Y+3	RESTR
GOAL			1 000 000.		1000.		1.		
SALE 1	1.								≤ 6.
SALE 2		1.							≤ 10.
CAPACITY	10.	20.							≤ 160.
CASH	300.	200.					-1.	1.	= 2 400.
WORKCAPL	600.	200.			1.	-1.			= 4 000.
CONTRIB	600.	200.	1.	-1.					= 4 700.
C-DEVLIM								1.	≤ 500.

VARIABLE TYPE	ENTRIES	SOLUTION ACTIVITY	UPPER BOUND	LOWER BOUND	CURRENT COST	REDUCED COST
X1 B*	5	6.000	***********	0.000	0.000	0.000
SALE1 UL	0	6.000	6.000	0.000	0.000	***********
CAPACITYUL	0	160.000	160.000	0.000	0.000	***********
CASH EQ	0	2400.000	2400.000	2400.000	0.000	0.000
WORKCAPLEQ	0	4000.000	4000.000	4000.000	0.000	0.000
CONTRIB EQ	0	4700.000	4700.000	4700.000	0.000	***********
X2 B*	5	5.000	***********	0.000	0.000	0.000
SALE2 B*	0	5.000	10.000	0.000	0.000	0.000
Y-1 B*	2	100.000	***********	0.000	1000000.001	0.000
GOAL B*	0	100000002.687	***********	***********	-1.000	1.000
Y+1 LL	1	0.000	***********	0.000	0.000	***********
Y-2 LL	2	0.000	***********	0.000	1000.000	-1000.000
Y+2 B*	1	600.000	***********	0.000	0.000	0.000
Y-3 B*	3	400.000	***********	0.000	1.000	-0.000
C-DEVLIMB*	0	400.000	500.000	0.000	0.000	0.000
Y+3 LL	1	0.000	***********	0.000	0.000	0.000

Table 6-1. The Optimal Solution of the Goal Programming Problem.

The third and least important goal cannot be reached completely. The negative deviation from the goal of the ending cash balance of $ 500 is $ 400: $y_3^- = 400$. The closing balance is therefore $ 100.

The solution is typical of goal programming. We can meet some goals completely and others partially. It is also typical that a lower priority goal can be completely met while there is a negative deviation from a higher priority goal. We overachieved the working capital goal although there is a negative deviation from the more important contribution goal.

	Total	Product A	Product B
Sales	$ 9 400	900(6) = 5 400	800(5) = 4 000
Variable Cost	4 800	300(6) = 1 800	600(5) = 3 000
Contribution	4 600	3 600	1 000
Fixed Costs			
Depreciation	500		
Paid in Cash	1 900		
Other	800	3 200	
Profit		1 400	

Table 6-2. Projected Income Statement.

Current Assets			Liabilities			
Cash		100	Accounts Payable		800	
Accounts Receivable			Old Loans		7 900	
A (1)900(6) =	5 400		New Loans		1 200	9 900
B (0.5)800(5) =	2 000	7 400	Equity			
Inventories		6 000	Beg. Balance	7 400		
Fixed Assets			Profit	1 400	8 800	
Beg. Balance	4 500		Dividends		700	8 100
Acquisitions	500 5 000					
Depreciation	500	4 500				
Total		$ 18 000	Total			$ 18 000

Table 6-3. Projected Balance Sheet.

Cash	$ 100
Accounts Receivable	7 400
Inventories	6 000
Subtotal	13 500
Short-Term Liabilities	9 900
Working Capital Ending Balance	3 600

Table 6-4. Working Capital Ending Balance.

Planning Dividend Policy

A defect of the present-day financial theory is that we do not know how the financial market reacts to changes in dividend policy. Looking at actual behavioral alternatives we can distinguish between two extreme cases and an infinite number of alternatives between these two extremes.

An extreme alternative is to follow the policy where all dividends are currently distributed and whenever additional equity is needed new shares are issued. The opposite is the firm which never distributes dividends. The obvious reason for nondistribution must be that the management considers to be able to make a better use of the funds generated by the firm than the shareholder to whom the dividends should be distributed. The better use is normally the internal growth of the firm.

The double taxation of the dividend income may easily lead to the conclusion that the firm should retain the profit undistributed to be used for expansion. However, there is some doubt even at the theoretical level as to the correctness of this conclusion. Moreover, some empirical findings have led to the disturbing result according to which there is no positive correlation between the retention rate and the growth rate of the firm. Rather, the contrary seems to be true.

While theoreticians discuss the problem and new empirical research is carried out managements must make decisions on dividend policy. Very few firms follow either of the extreme policies referred to above. A part of the profit is normally distributed and the rest retained. Another feature often found in practice is that a dividend policy once adopted is maintained without changes for several years. A reason for this could be that the management regards a change in dividend policy to be an important event which signals to the shareholders a change in the future prospects of the firm's development.

In order to prepare ourselves for the presentation of a strategic planning model to be presented in the following chapter we will now consider a simple example of dividend policy decision. The amount of dividends is to be decided within a given policy and depending on the amount of profit which is unknown before the solution of the model. We will consider a firm which makes two products in two production departments. The sales prices, variable costs, and standard production times are as follows:

	Product A	Product B
Sales Price, $/unit	2.50	1.50
Variable Cost	1.50	1.-
Contribution	1.-	0.50
Capacity Used in Production		
Assembly, hours/unit	3	2
Machining　》　》	5	

The available production capacity is 12 hours in the Assembly Department and 10 hours in the Machining Department. The fixed costs are $ 2.- and they are all paid in cash. Both the sales and the production costs are paid in cash.

The profit goal is $ 4.- before tax. Since the fixed costs are $ 2.-, the contribution goal is $ 6.-. This is the most important goal. The negative deviation from this goal must be minimized with the highest order of priority. The overachievement of this goal is permitted but not actively sought.

Let us assume that 50 percent of the profit before tax is paid in taxes. The net profit is available for dividends or for retention and the subsequent use for financing the expansion of the firm. The second goal is to maintain a given level of dividends. This level is $ 1.-. If the contribution goal is completely achieved the net profit will be $ 2.-. A $ 1.- dividend then implies a 50 percent payout policy.

We assume that management wants to maintain the dividends of $ 1.- even if it means a higher payout than 50 percent. The negative deviation from the dividend goal is therefore to be avoided. On the other hand, management does not want to distribute a dividend higher than $ 1.-, i.e., we do not even add the positive deviation to the respective constraint.

The third goal is the full utilization of the production capacity. Overtime work is not permitted. It follows that the firm has three levels of goals, profit, dividends, and capacity utilization.

The following variables are used in the model:

x_1 = production and sale of product A,

x_2 = production and sale of product B,

x_3 = profit before tax,

x_4 = dividends,

y_1^- = underutilization of production capacity, assy dept.,

y_2^- = underutilization of production capacity, machining dept.,

y_3^- = negative deviation from contribution,

y_3^+ = positive deviation from contribution,

y_4 = undistributed profit,

y_5^- = negative deviation from the target dividends.

We first write out the production capacity constraints. Due to variables y_1^- and y_2^- that represent underutilization these constraints are now equalities:

$$(6\text{-}5) \quad \begin{aligned} 3x_1 + 2x_2 + y_1^- &= 12 \\ 5x_1 \qquad\qquad + y_2^- &= 10. \end{aligned}$$

The next equation set the actual contribution in relation to the goal on contribution. Both positive and negative deviation is possible from this goal:

$$(6\text{-}6) \quad 1x_1 + 0.5x_2 + y_3^- - y_3^+ = 6.$$

Profit before tax is by definition the total contribution less fixed costs. By rearrangement we get the equation:

$$(6\text{-}7) \quad x_1 + 0.5x_2 - x_3 = 2.$$

The upper limit of dividends is the net profit which is again 50 percent of the profit before tax. If the actual dividends are less than the net profit, variable y_4 takes the slack, i.e., shows the amount of undistributed profit.

$$(6\text{-}8) \quad x_4 + y_4 = 0.5x_3, \text{ or } 0.5x_3 - x_4 - y_4 = 0.$$

Finally, the actual dividends and the negative deviation from the dividend goal must equal the goal:

$$(6\text{-}9) \quad x_4 + y_5^- = 1.$$

All variables must of course be nonnegative.

The least important goal is the capacity utilization. Therefore, the priority factor M_1 is associated with variables y_1^- and y_2^-. The next goal is the payment of dividends. To show this, the priority factor M_2 is associated with variable y_5^-. The most important goal is the total contribution. The highest priority factor M_3 is therefore associated with variable y_3^-. The objective function to be minimized can now be written as

$$(6\text{-}10) \quad \text{Min } Z = M_1 y_1^- + M_1 y_2^- + M_3 y_3^- + M_2 y_5^-.$$

Because we again want to solve the problem using the normal linear programming routine, we replace the priorities M_3, M_2, and M_1 by real numbers 1 000 000, 1 000, and 1:

$$(6\text{-}10') \quad \text{Min } Z = 1y_1^- + 1y_2^- + 1\,000\,000 y_3^- + 1\,000 y_5^-.$$

The solution of the problem is given in Table 6-5. The contribution goal is not completely achieved. The variable giving the negative deviation from this goal is at a positive level:

$$y_3^- = 2.5.$$

The projected income statement is as follows:

Contribution		
Product A	1(2) = 2.–	
Product B	0.5(3) = 1.5	3.5
Fixed Costs		2.–
Profit before Tax		1.5
Income Tax		0.75
Net Operating Profit		0.75

It follows that we cannot distribute the target dividends. The negative deviation from the dividend goal is $ 0.25 and the actual dividends are $ 0.75:

$$y_5^- = 0.25 \text{ and } x_4 = 0.75.$$

The lower priority goals are exactly achieved:

$$y_1^- = 0 \text{ and } y_2^- = 0.$$

The structure of the example was such that the available production capacity prevented the achievement of the higher goals. It was stated at the beginning of the example that the management does not want to overexceed the dividend goal. We will next relax the capacity constraints so that this feature of the model can also be demonstrated.

We assume that the firm considers the employment of the second shift in production. In other words, we allow the overutilization of the production capacity by adding variables y_1^+ and y_2^+ to the capacity constraints. On the other hand, we set upper limits to both deviations. These upper limits are equal to the available second shift capacity.

Providing for the second shift involves additional fixed costs. These costs are $ 0.75. They are added to the original fixed costs in the profit constraint. The new variant of the model is:

	X1	X2	X3	X4	Y-1	Y-2	Y-3	Y+3	Y4	Y-5	RESTRIC
GOAL					1.	1.	1 000 000.			1 000.	
ASSY	3.	2.			1.						= 12.
MACHINE	5.					1.					= 10.
CONTRIB	1.	0.5					1.	-1.			= 6.
PROFIT	1.	0.5	-1.								= 2.
DIVIDLIM			0.5	-1.					-1.		= 0.
DIVIGOAL				1.						1.	= 1.

VARIABLE	ENTRIES TYPE		SOLUTION ACTIVITY	UPPER BOUND	LOWER BOUND	CURRENT COST	REDUCED COST
X1	B*	4	2.000	***********	0.000	0.000	0.000
ASSY	EQ	0	12.000	12.000	12.000	0.000	26.250
MACHINE	EQ	0	10.000	10.000	10.000	0.000	5.250
CONTRIB	EQ	0	6.000	6.000	6.000	0.000	-100.000
PROFIT	EQ	0	2.000	2.000	2.000	0.000	-5.000
X2	B*	3	3.000	***********	0.000	0.000	0.000
X3	B*	2	1.500	***********	0.000	0.000	0.000
DIVIDLIMEQ		0	0.000	0.000	0.000	0.000	-9.999
X4	B*	2	0.749	***********	0.000	0.000	0.000
DIVIGOALEQ		0	1.000	1.000	1.000	0.000	-10.000
Y-1	LL	2	0.000	***********	0.000	1.000	-27.250
GOAL	B*	0	252.499	***********	***********	-1.000	1.000
Y-2	LL	2	0.000	***********	0.000	1.000	-6.250
Y+3	LL	2	0.000	***********	0.000	-100.000	0.000
Y-3	B*	2	2.499	***********	0.000	100.000	0.000
Y4	LL	1	0.000	***********	0.000	0.000	-9.999
Y-5	B*	2	0.250	***********	0.000	10.000	0.000

Table 6-5. The Optimal Solution of the Dividend Problem.

$$\text{Min } Z = \qquad y_1^- + y_2^- + 100y_3^- \qquad\qquad + 10y_5^-$$

subject to

$$3x_1 + 2x_2 \qquad\quad + y_1^- - y_1^+ \qquad\qquad\qquad\qquad = 12$$
$$5x_1 \qquad\qquad\qquad\quad + y_2^- - y_2^+ \qquad\qquad\qquad = 10$$
$$x_1 + 0.5x_2 \qquad\qquad\qquad\quad + y_3^- - y_3^+ \qquad = 6$$
$$x_1 + 0.5x_2 - \quad x_3 \qquad\qquad\qquad\qquad\qquad = 2.75$$
$$0.5x_3 - x_4 \qquad\qquad\qquad - y_4 = 0$$
$$x_4 \qquad\qquad\qquad\qquad + y_5^- = 1$$
$$y_1^+ \qquad\qquad\qquad\qquad \leq 12$$
$$y_2^+ \qquad\qquad\qquad \leq 10$$

and all variables nonnegative.

It is now possible to achieve all goals. The optimal program of the problem is:

$$x_1 = 4, \qquad y_1^- = 0,\ y_1^+ = 12,\ y_3^- = 0,\ y_4 = 1.125,$$
$$x_2 = 6, \qquad y_2^- = 0,\ y_2^+ = 10,\ y_3^+ = 1,\ y_5^- = 0,$$
$$x_3 = 4.25,$$
$$x_4 = 1.$$

There is an overachievement of the contribution goal of \$ 1.- ($y_3^+ = 1$) and the amount of undistributed profit is \$ 1.125 ($y_4 = 0.125$). We actually should have increased the contribution goal simultaneously with the increase in the fixed costs due to the second shift. In addition, to show a realistic cost behavior we might have added variables y_1^+ and y_2^+ to profit constraint (6-7) with (negative) cost coefficients. These cost coefficients might be due to shift premiums, etc. The overachievement of the contribution goal could then easily turn into an underachievement.

Capital Structure, Growth and Dividends

The dividend policy problem limits our attention to the equity section of the balance sheet. The alternatives to finance growth in such a model are retained earnings and new issues of share capital. However, strategic planning cannot be limited to these two alternative forms of finance. Debt financing should also be considered. This brings our attention to the debt/equity ratio and the amount of new debt that can be taken over the planning horizon.

The problem of the optimal capital structure has not found any more conclusive solution in the financial literature than the problem of optimal dividend policy. There are a number of theorists who maintain that all structures are equally good and there are others who say that there is an optimal structure. While the question is being debated the management must make decisions about the actual structure of real firms. It has to use either subjective estimates or guidelines set by the creditors of the firm.

We will now expand the problem (6-3) and (6-4) to include the possibility of debt financing. In it the original example of chapter 1 was already expanded by the inclusion of new short-term loans in the amount of $ 1 200 and by the payment of dividends in the amount of $ 700. Instead of considering new loans and dividends as given amounts we will convert them into variables and make their values dependent on the dividend and capital structure policy.

The following variables are used in the model:

x_1 = production and sale of product A,

x_2 = production and sale of product B,

z = profit after tax (the value of this variable also indicates the amount of income tax for we assume that the income tax rate is 50 percent),

w = dividends,

u = new short-term loans (the 10 percent interest on these loans must be paid in advance),

y_1^- = negative deviation from the dividend goal,

y_2^- = negative deviation from the working capital goal,

y_2^+ = positive deviation from the working capital goal,

y_3^- = negative deviation of debt from the maximum amount of debt allowed by the capital structure goal,

y_3^+ = positive deviation of debt from the maximum amount allowed by the capital structure goal.

We assume that the firm has three goals. The most important goal is dividends which must remain at least at a given level. This level is $ 1 500. The next goal is a given level of working capital. The ending

balance of working capital should be at least $ 3 000. The third goal is
a given capital structure. The amount of liabilities can be at most
60 percent of the sum of liabilities and equity. The minimum cash
balance can now be achieved because the firm has the possibility to
take new loans. In this example we omit the contribution goal and let
the dividend goal take care of the level of profit required.

The marketing and production constraints of the model have not
changed from the preceding versions:

$$
(6\text{-}11) \quad
\begin{aligned}
x_1 &\le 6 \\
x_2 &\le 10 \\
10x_1 + 20x_2 &\le 160.
\end{aligned}
$$

To formulate the cash constraint we must first take into account the
fixed cash receipts and expenses:

Fixed Cash Receipts		
Beginning Balance	$ 1 000	
Accounts Receivable Balance	6 800	7 800
Fixed Cash Expenses		
Accounts Payable Balance	900	
Repayment of Loans	2 100	
Fixed Expenses	1 900	
Capital Budget	500	5 400
Cash Available		$ 2 400

The cash constraint is next formulated by requiring that the beginning
balance plus fixed and variable cash receipts are equal to the fixed and
variable cash expenses plus the ending balance:

$$7\,800 + (0)900x_1 + (0.5)x_2 + u = 5\,400 + 300x_1 + 600x_2 + 0.1u + w + 500.$$

The constraint reduces to

$$(6\text{-}12) \quad 300x_1 + 200x_2 - 0.9u + w = 1\,900.$$

The working capital constraint is also formulated in the usual way by
beginning with the working capital balance at the beginning of the period
and taking into account all possible sources for changes in this balance.
The resulting ending balance is then associated with the deviations and
the goal:

$$2\,900 + 900x_1 + 800x_2 - 300x_1 - 600x_2 - 2\,700 - z - w - 500 - 0.1u +$$
$$+ y_2^- - y_2^+ = 3\,000.$$

After simplification the constraint is

(6-13) $600x_1 + 200x_2 - 0.1u - w - z + y_2^- - y_2^+ = 3\ 300$.

The amount of working capital is now reduced by interest, $0.1u$, dividends, w, and income taxes, z, which all involve a credit to the working capital account and a debit to some other account.

The constraint on the capital structure includes in this example all liabilities. The debt-to-equity ratio is commonly computed without the inclusion of the accounts payable balance. However, the capital structure of the present example is overly simplified in that the firm does not have any long-term debt. We therefore demonstrate the use of the capital structure ratio constraint by taking the existing liabilities into consideration. This will be sufficient for demonstrating how to use ratio constraints in strategic models.

We assume that the goal is to maintain the liabilities below the level of 60 percent of the sum of the liabilities and the equity at the end of the period. In other words, the liabilities can be at most 1.5 times the equity. However, if more important goals so require, this ratio can be exceeded. A negative deviation from this goal is of course permitted. We get the following constraint:

$(10\ 000 - 2\ 100) + 800 + u + z \leq 1.5(7\ 400 + z - w)$.

The first term on the left-hand side, $10\ 000 - 2\ 100$, is the beginning balance of the loans less repayments. The next term, 800, is the accrued fixed expenses of the period. The ending balance of new loans is given by the value of variable u and the accrued income taxes by z. The right-hand side is the beginning balance of the equity, $7\ 400$, plus the net profit for the period, z, less the dividends to be paid at the end of the period, w. By adding the variables for deviations we get

(6-14) $-0.5z + u + 1.5w + y_3^- - y_3^+ = 2\ 400$.

We assume that the beginning balance of equity, \$ 7 400, includes retained earnings in the amount of \$ 400. If so desired, this amount can be distributed as dividends. The upper limit of dividends is therefore the net profit for the period plus the earnings retained in the preceding periods:

(6-15) $w \leq z + 400$.

The dividend goal is \$ 1 500. The actual dividends plus any negative deviation from this goal must equal \$ 1 500:

(6-16) $w + y_1^- = 1\ 500.$

The amount of the net profit is determined by the contribution, the interest of new loans, and the fixed costs. The income tax rate is 50 percent. Hence, the profit before tax is given by 2z. We get the following equation:

(6-17) $600x_1 + 200x_2 - 0.1u - 2z = 3\ 200.$

The most important goal is to minimize the negative deviation from the dividend goal. The second goal is to minimize the negative deviation from the working capital balance. The third and the least important goal is to minimize the positive deviation from the maximum amount of liabilities that can exist in relation to the existing equity. The objective function is therefore

(6-18) Min $Z = M_3 y_1^- + M_2 y_2^- + M_1 y_3^+.$

When we replace the pre-emptive priorities with suitable real numbers and solve the problem as a normal linear programming problem, we get the following optimal program:

$x_1 = 6,$ $y_1^- = 505.263,$

$x_2 = 5,$ $y_2^- = 500,$

$z\ \ = 594.736,$ $y_3^+ = 900,$

$w\ \ = 994.736,$

$u\ \ = 2\ 105.263.$

None of the goals can be completely achieved in this model. There is a negative deviation of \$ 505.26 from the most important goal of dividends. This is indicated by the value of variable y_1^- int the optimal program. The actual dividends are \$ 994.74 as indicated by the optimal value of variable w.

The negative deviation from the working capital goal is \$ 500. The liabilities exceed the maximum amount permitted by the capital structure goal by \$ 900.

The projected financial statements drawn up on the basis of the optimal solution have been presented in Tables 6-6 to 6-9.

	Total	Product A	Product B
Sales	$ 9 400	5 400	4 000
Variable Costs	4 800	1 800	3 000
Contribution	4 600	3 600	1 000
Interest Expenses	210.53		
Subtotal	4 389.47		
Fixed Costs	3 200		
Profit before Tax	1 189.47		
Income Tax	594.73		
Net Profit	594.74		

Table 6-6. Projected Income Statement.

Current Assets

				Liabilities		
Cash	500			Accounts Payable	800	
Accounts Receivable	7 400			Accrued Taxes	594.74	
Inventories	6 000	13 900		Old Loans	7 900	
Fixed Assets				New Loans	2 105.26	11 400
Beg. Balance	4 500			**Equity**		
Capital Budget	500			Beg. Balance	7 400	
	5 000			Net Profit	594.74	
Depreciation	500	4 500			7 994.74	
				Dividends	994.74	7 000
		$ 18 400				$ 18 400

Table 6-7. Projected Balance Sheet.

Current Assets	$ 13 900
Current Liabilities	11 400
Projected Working Capital	2 500
Negative Deviation y_2^-	500
Working Capital Goal	$ 3 000

Table 6-8. Projected Working Capital.

Liabilities	$ 11 400
150 Percent of Equity	10 500
Positive Deviation y_3^+	900

Table 6-9. Projected Capital Structure.

Problems

6-1. Consider a firm making and selling three products. The sales prices, variable costs, and standard production times of the products are as follows:

	Products		
	A	B	C
Production and Sales, units	x_1	x_2	x_3
Sales Price, $/unit	3.-	5.-	8.-
Variable Costs, $/unit	1.5	3.-	5.-
Contribution, $/unit	1.5	2.-	3.-
Required Capacity, hours/unit			
Machining	1	2	3
Assembly	2	1.5	1

All products go through both machining and assembly department. The available production capacity is 120 hours in the machining department and 170 hours in the assembly. This is the net available capacity. (The firm plans to increase the level of inventories and the capacity required for this purpose has been deducted from the total capacity to arrive at the figures given above. By this device we can use the variables x_j for both production and sales.)

The beginning balance for the period is as follows:

Cash	$ 50	Accounts Payable	$ 80
Accounts Receivable	70	Long-Term Loans	200
Inventories	150	Equity	290
Fixed Assets	300		
	$ 570		$ 570

The fixed cost budget for the period has been broken down to depreciation, expenses to be paid in cash during the planning period, and accrued expenses to be paid beyond the horizon:

Depreciation	$ 30.-
Cash Expenses	30.-
Accruals	20.-
Total Fixed Expenses	$ 80.-

The scheduled repayments of the existing long-term loans are $ 15. The total capital budget for the period is $ 60. All items in the budget are paid in cash. The planned dividends are $ 20.-, and the planned increase in the level of inventories amounts to $ 10.

The cash collections from sales are 50 percent in the same period the products are sold and the remainder in the following period. The terms of payment of variable costs are 60 percent cash and the remainder in the following period. New short-term loans are available if additional funds are needed. The rate of interest on the new loans is 10 percent. The interest is charged against the income for the period. However, it is paid back together with the principal after the horizon.

The most important goal of the management is to achieve a total before-tax profit of $ 60. Overachievement of this goal is permitted although the firm does not actively strive for it.

The second goal is to achieve a level of working capital of $ 200. This goal can also be overachieved although it is not actively sought.

The third goal is to achieve a closing cash balance of $ 20. Both the negative and the positive deviation from this goal must be avoided. In addition, the ending cash balance cannot, of course, be negative.

Required:

Develop a goal programming model for this problem, solve it, and develop the projected financial statements as well as the statement for working capital.

6-2. Some of the data listed below is unnecessary for the required formulation of the problem:

(a) The beginning balance sheet of the firm is the following:

Beginning Balance Sheet			
Cash	$ 10	Accounts Payable	$ 15
Accounts Receivable	50	Bonds	85
Finished Products	30	Equity	100
Raw Materials	20		
Fixed Assets	90		
	$ 200		$ 200

(b) The required closing balance of cash is $ 15 at the end of the first period. At least the same balance must be maintained at the end of the second period.

(c) The beginning balance of accounts receivable is collected and the beginning balance of accounts payable is paid in the first period.

(d) The ending balance of finished products is maintained at its original level at the end of the first period. It will be reduced by $ 20 by the end of the second period.

155

(e) The raw material inventory is kept at the level of the beginning balance at the end of both periods. The raw material price is $ 3.- per unit. The number of units purchased is denoted by variable z_i, $i = 1.2$. The terms of payment of raw material purchases are 40 percent cash and the remainder in the following period.

(f) The sales price of the finished products is $ 2.- per unit. The sales in period i are denoted by variable x_i.

(g) The variable production costs are $ 0.50 per unit of product. The fixed costs are $ 5.- in both periods and they are all paid in cash.

(h) The capital budget is $ 10 in the second period. All capital expenditures are paid in cash. Depreciation charges are $ 4.- in both periods.

Required:

Formulate constraints for a two-period model which require that the ending balance of working capital is at least $ 90.at the end of the first period and $ 100 at the end of the second period.

6-3. The firm has the following beginning balance:

Beginning Balance

Cash	$ 10	Accounts Payable	$ 16
Accounts Receivable	15	Bonds	21
Inventories	12	Equity	20
Fixed Assets	20		
	$ 57		$ 57

The firm makes and sells two products, A and B. The available production capacity is 18 hours. The following cost and production data is available about the products:

	A	B
Sales Price, $/unit (cash)	5.-	8.-
Variable Costs »	3.-	5.-
Required Capacity, hours/unit	2	1.5

The beginning balance of accounts receivable is collected and that of accounts payable paid during the period. The fixed costs are $ 6 and they are paid in cash. The amortization of bonds is $ 4. There are no changes in the amount of inventories.

Required:

Formulate a goal programming problem with the following goals which are given in the order of decreasing importance:

(a) The most important goal is profit. It should be as close to $ 15 as possible. Overachievement is permitted. (Taxes are disregarded.)

(b) The ending balance of working capital must be as close to $ 20 as possible.

(c) The ending balance of cash should be at least $ 8. The negative deviation from this goal must not exceed this amount. Positive deviation is permitted.

In addition, it is to be observed that the capacity used in production must not exceed the available capacity.

6-4. We are developing a two-period model for a firm with the following balance sheet (only the relevant items are shown):

Accounts Payable			$ 100
Long-Term Loans			1 600
Equity			
Shareholders' Capital		1 000	
Retained Earnings			
Beginning Balance	150		
Profit for the Period	50	200	1 200

The only item in Accounts Payable balance is dividends declared but not yet paid, i.e., the net profit for the period totals $ 150 and the management has decided to distribute $ 100 and retains $ 50. The repayments of long-term loans are $ 125 in both periods. The firm can take new loans in both periods. The repayments of these loans are 20 percent in each period that follows the period when the loan is taken. The following variables are used in the model:

v_j = the amount of new loans taken in period j,

x_j = the after-tax profit in period j,

y^-_{1j} = the negative deviation from the goal of earnings growth in period j,

y^-_{2j} = the negative deviation from the goal of minimum dividends in period j.

<u>Required</u>:

(a) Formulate a constraint for both periods which requires that the amount of existing and new loans must not exceed 60 percent of the sum of loans and equity.

(b) Formulate constraints which require that the growth of earnings must be 15 percent per period. A negative deviation from this goal is permitted.

(c) Formulate constraints which require that the minimum dividends are 105 percent of the actual dividends of the preceding period. A negative deviation from this goal is permitted.

7 Strategic Planning with Goal Programming

Strategic vs. Tactical Planning

The discussion in the first four chapters of the present text has been dealing with models belonging to the area of strategic planning. The objective function of all these models is the maximization of the contribution or a variant thereof. The maximization was carried out subject to a set of constraints. The available production capacity is a member of this set in every model. In other words, we have been carrying out short-term planning which does not allow changes in the fixed production capacity. Some of the models included capital budget in the source data but the size and the composition of the budget was always determined outside the model.

Things which are taken as given in tactical planning are the subject of strategic plans. One of these subjects is capital budgeting, i.e., the determination of the available production capacity in future periods.

The analysis of investment projects has a long tradition in accounting literature. Traditional planning techniques center on the time value of money and discounting of future amounts to the present with the cost of capital. The budget models, on the other hand, operate with nominal values.

The problem usually treated in traditional investment analysis is the question whether a project is profitable or not. Firms normally have several projects simultaneously available. The second question is, therefore, which projects should be included in the capital budget.

Analysis of investment decisions has developed rapidly in the 1960´s. Linear programming was applied to the problem by Wingartner to relax the restrictive assumptions of the traditional discounting methods.[1] Linear programming, however, is not without limitations either. The most important limitation is the basic assumption that all projects are

---

1 Weingartner, H. Martin, <u>Mathematical Programming and the Analysis of Capital Budgeting Problems</u> (Englewood Cliffs, N.J.: Prentice-Hall, 1963).

perfectly divisible. Integer programming was introduced to avoid this difficulty. Quadratic programming, chance constrained programming, etc. have been employed to take risk into account. It is not possible to make a complete survey of these developments in the present text.

Even the recent advances in the analysis of investment projects share a common feature with traditional methods. This is the analysis of investment projects in isolation from the existing operations. The separation of investment decisions from operating decisions is due to the traditional way of developing budgets in the accounting literature. However, it was realized by several authors in the latter part of the 1960's that the separation of investment decisions from operations is largely artificial. In strategic planning we should therefore combine into a single model the analysis of investment projects and the planning of operations.

Strategic planning, however, is more than the analysis of investment projects. A distinctive feature of strategic planning is the analysis of the goals of the management. Normally top management has several goals which are contradictory. It follows that strategic planning cannot be based on models which maximize a single objective such as the long-run profit contribution of a production program. As we have noted, the models used for generating annual budgets are, on the other hand, built under the assumption that in the short run the best that a firm can do is to maximize the total contribution subject to a fixed production capacity and other constraints.

Since an attempt to extend a profit maximizing budget model to cover several years would often lead to an unrealistic representation of the problem facing the management, we must look for other techniques. It is the purpose of the present chapter to demonstrate how goal programming techniques can be used to handle multiple goals.

The model will be built around a hypothetical small firm in order to keep the treatment as simple as possible. However, the model can easily be generalized to deal with more complicated situations. The example will be complicated enough to demonstrate how both the physical and financial aspects of strategic planning can be integrated into a single formalized plan.

The Corporation, Its Objectives and Environment

A strategic plan usually covers the objectives of the corporation as well as the means available for the achievement of these goals. The plan must also take into account the constraints which the environment places on the corporation. The development of any plan begins with an analysis of the corporation, its goals, and environment. We assume that this analysis has already been carried out and briefly list the results.

We first assume that top management has carried out an anlysis of its goal structure and has come up with the following tentative set of goals. The most important goal is the continuation of the present dividend policy. Dividends have been declared on a given level and this level has been gradually raised over the years. Management believes that the dividends in the near future should be as close to this level as possible and that they should be increased by 10 percent each year of the horizon. On the other hand, management believes that there is no need to increase the dividends over the prescribed goal even if the profit position indicates that this would be possible. The remaining profit can be invested back into the firm to increase its rate of growth. If the dividend goals cannot be completely met, management has no definite preference as to when dividends should fall short of the goals and all years are treated alike in the model in this respect.

A second goal is the growth of net after tax earnings. Profit should grow from year to year. However, management feels that it is more important to achieve the desired growth in the near future than in later years. Therefore, the negative deviations from the earnings growth targets will be weighted with a discount factor. The management's subjective rate of interest is 20 percent.

The growth of earnings is only one measure of the firm's growth. Another often used measure is the growth of sales. We assume that the management has selected the growth of sales as a third order goal. The objective is to increase sales each year by 20 percent from the level of the preceding year. If this goal cannot be achieved completely, management does not have any preference as to when negative deviations may occur. The first year the sales goal is assumed to be $ 320.

The least important goal concerns the capital structure. If more important goals require the use of debt, the capital structure may temporarily deteriorate, but it must return to a prescribed level by the end of the last year of the planning horizon.

As is normal in strategic planning, these management goals have been expressed in financial terms. However, physical resources must be secured to achieve these goals. Investments must be made in plant and equipment to increase sales and profits, etc. We next turn to environmental and internal factors that must be observed in the plan. The present model will be restricted to three periods. However, it will be clear from the structure of the model how additional periods could be included in the model in actual applications.

The firm can make and sell two products. The estimated selling prices and costs are listed below. Product A has a lower selling price and unit contribution but it also requires less production capacity than product B:

	Products	
	A	B
Selling price, $/unit	3.-	8.-
Variable cost, $/unit	1.5	5.-
Contribution margin, $/unit	1.5	3.-
Required production capacity, hours/unit	1	3

Available production capacity is 100 hours/period in each year if no new investments in the production capacity are made. The firm can invest in new capacity by building two additional production units. Technical considerations permit the construction of the first unit in the first year and the second unit in the second year. Alternatively, both new units can be built in the second year if this is found to be desirable. Each new unit adds 20 hours of production capacity per period beginning from the year following the project´s completion. In other words, if we build a new unit in the first year, it can begin production in the second year. The construction of a unit costs $ 60 and there are no significant economies of scale if both units are constructed simultaneously. Investment in new production capacity must be paid in cash in the year of its completion.

The firm´s position in financial terms is indicated by the following balance sheet:

Beginning Balance Sheet

Assets			Liabilities		
Cash		$ 50	Accounts Payable		$ 80
Accounts Receivable		70	Long-Term Debt		200
Inventories		150	Equity		
Fixed Assets		300	Share Capital	250	
			Undistributed Profit	40	290
		$ 570			$ 570

Cash balance is to be maintained at least at the level of $ 20 at the end of each period. No additional investment in inventories are needed even if production capacity is increased. Accounts Receivable will be determined by the development of sales. It is assumed that cash collections amount to 50 percent of the sales revenue. The remainder is collected in the following period. Accounts Payable are determined by the variable costs of production of which 60 percent are paid in the period they are incurred and the remainder in the following period.

The firm must reserve each period $ 15 for the amortization of long-term debt. If the firm needs new debt financing it can take short-term bank loans in any reasonable amounts. The interest of these loans is 10 percent and it is paid back together with the principal one year after it has been taken. However, as far as the profit planning is concerned interest on new loans is considered already in the year when the loan is taken. Dividends already declared but not yet paid at the beginning of the first period are $ 20. This amount is included in the figure for undistributed profit in the beginning balance. Funds must be reserved for the payment of these dividends in the first year of the plan.

The following budget has been developed for fixed expenses in each year of the horizon:

	Period		
	1	2	3
Fixed Expenses			
Depreciation of Existing Fixed Assets	$ 30	$ 27	$ 25
Fixed Expenses Payable in Cash	30	33	35
Accrued Fixed Expenses to Be Paid in the Next Period	20	22	24
	$ 80	$ 82	$ 84

Accrued fixed expenses must be reflected in cash payments of the year following the accrual.

Depreciation of fixed assets is normally considered a fixed charge. However, in the present situation we do not know before the solution of the model whether the firm will invest in new production capacity and if it does, when this investment will take place. We must therefore take the depreciation of fixed assets acquired over the horizon into account with the help of variables. It will suffice to mention at this point that 30 percent of the balance of fixed assets can be depreciated each year.

Corporate income tax rate is 50 percent. The tax is paid in the year following the year for which profit is declared.

It was stated above that the fourth level management goal is the preservation of capital structure. It will be assumed that the maximum amount of debt to be allowed is 60 percent of the sum of debt and equity. Accrued income taxes and dividends are not included in the constraint that determines the capital structure.

The Model

The Variables

The following variables are needed to develop the model:

q_i = investment in new production capacity in period i,

x_{1i} = production and sales of product A in period i,

x_{2i} = production and sales of product B in period i,

y_i = new bank loans takes in period i,

z_i = net after tax earnings in period i (since the income tax rate is 0.5, profit before tax is $2z_i$),

u_i = dividend declared at the end of period i,

v_{i1} = slack of production capacity in period i,

v_{i2}^- = negative deviation of debt from the maximum amount of debt allowed by the capital structure goal in period i,

v_{i2}^+ = positive deviation of debt from the maximum amount allowed in period i,

v_{i3} = cash in excess of the required minimum balance in period i, i.e., slack of liquidity constraint,

v_{i4} = undistributed profit in period i,

v_{i5}^- = negative deviation from the dividend goal in period i,

v_{i6}^- = negative deviation from the goal of earnings growth in period i,

v_{i7}^- = negative deviation from the sales goal in period i,

v_{i8} = underutilization of technically feasible investment program in period i,
(i = 1, 2, 3).

The Constraints

Capacity Constraints: We begin to build the model by observing that physical production plans must not exceed the available production capacity in any year of the horizon

(1)
$$x_{11} + 3x_{12} + v_{11} = 100,$$
$$x_{21} + 3x_{22} + v_{21} = 100 + 20q_1,$$
$$x_{31} + 3x_{32} + v_{31} = 100 + 20q_1 + 20q_2.$$

The first equation relates the capacity used in the first year production program, $x_{11} + 3x_{12}$, and any possible unused capacity, v_{11}, to the total available capacity, 100 hours. If the firm constructs q_1 units of new plants in the first year, this will increase the production capacity by 20 hours from the beginning of the second year. The constraints for the other two years therefore state that the capacity used by the production of the year plus any possible underutilization must not exceed the capacity available initially plus the capacity acquired by the beginning of the year.

Upper Limits of New Plant Construction: It is technically feasible to build at most one new plant unit in the first year and two plants in the first two years. It is also possible to postpone the building of both units until the second year. It is finally possible not to build any units at all if the investment turns out to be inadvisable for whatever reason. These relations are taken into account by the following two constraints:

(2)
$$q_1 \qquad + v_{18} \qquad = 1,$$
$$q_1 + q_2 \qquad + v_{28} = 2.$$

If, e.g., $q_1 = 1$, the interpretation is that one unit is built in the first period. If, in addition, the second unit is built, this is indicated by $q_2 = 1$. The combination $q_1 = 0$, and $q_2 = 2$ indicate that both units are built in the second period. If we get an answer that is in fractions, e.g., $q_1 = 0.8$, we may be in trouble. It may not make sense to build 80 peroent of the unit and have the production capacity increased by 80 percent. The present formulation of the model does not quarantee that noninteger solutions will never occur.

Profit before Tax

(3)
$$1.5x_{11} + 3x_{12} - 0.1y_1 - 2z_1 = 80,$$
$$1.5x_{21} + 3x_{22} - 0.1y_2 - (0.3)60q_1 - 2z_2 = 82,$$
$$1.5x_{31} + 3x_{32} - 0.1y_3 - (0.3)(1-0.3)60q_1 - (0.3)60q_2 - 2z_3 = 84$$

The first equation stipulates that the contribution margin of the sales of the first year, $1.5x_{11} + 3x_{12}$, less interest of new loans, $0.1y_1$, less profit before tax, $2z_1$, must equal the fixed expenses of the first year, 80. The depreciation of any new first year investment can begin in the second year. Therefore, the second year equation includes the term $(0.3)60q_1$ and the third year equation the term $(0.3)(1-0.3)60q_1$. Similarly, the third year equation includes the depreciation of the second year investment, $(0.3)60q_2$. We are assuming that the declining balance method of depreciation is applied and that the maximum allowable depreciation is 30 percent of the balance.

Constraints on the Capital Structure

(4)

$$(200-15) + y_1 + (0.4)(1.5x_{11} + 5x_{12}) + 20 + v_{12}^- - v_{12}^+ =$$
$$= (1.5)(290 - 20 + z_1 - u_1),$$

$$(200 - 15 - 15) + y_2 + (0.4)(1.5x_{21} + 5x_{22}) + 22 + v_{22}^- - v_{22}^+ =$$
$$= (1.5)(290 - 20 + z_1 + z_2 - u_1 - u_2),$$

$$(200 - 15 - 15 - 15) + y_3 + (0.4)(1.5x_{31} + 5x_{32}) + 24 + v_{32}^- =$$
$$= (1.5)(290 - 20 + z_1 + z_2 + z_3 - u_1 - u_2 - u_3).$$

The first year capital structure constraint relates the liabilities at the end of the year to the equity at the same point in time. The liabilities include the balance of long-term debt, $200 - 15$, the balance of new loans, y_1, the accounts payable for raw materials and wages, $(0.4)(1.5x_{11} + 5x_{12})$, and accrued fixed expenses, 20. Equity at the end of the first year is equity at the beginning of the year, $290 - 20$, plus net operating earnings, z_1, less dividends, u_1. A corresponding interpretation is given to other capital constraint equations. Both positive and negative deviations, $v_{12}^- - v_{12}^+$, can occur in the first two years. However, only a negative deviation is allowed to appear in the last year, i.e., debt cannot exceed the prescribed limit. Therefore, the variable v_{32}^+ does not appear in the third year equation.

Liquidity Constraints

(5)

$$(0.5)(3x_{11} + 8x_{12}) + y_1 - v_{13} = (80 + 30 + 15 + 20 + 20 - 50 - 70) +$$
$$+ 60q_1 + (0.6)(1.5x_{11} + 5x_{12}),$$

$$3x_{11} + 8x_{12} + (0.5)(3x_{21} + 8x_{22}) + y_2 - v_{23} = (45 + 33 + 15 + 20) +$$
$$+ 60q_1 + 60q_2 + 1.5x_{11} + 5x_{12} + (0.6)(1.5x_{21} + 5x_{22}) + 0.1y_1 +$$
$$+ u_1 + z_1,$$

$$3x_{11} + 8x_{12} + 3x_{21} + 8x_{22} + (0.5)(3x_{31} + 8x_{32}) + y_3 - v_{33} =$$
$$(113 + 35 + 60 + 15 + 22) + 60q_1 + 60q_2 + 1.5x_{11} + 5x_{12} +$$
$$+ 1.5x_{21} + 5x_{22} + (0.6)(1.5x_{31} + 5x_{32}) + 0.1y_1 + u_1 + u_2 +$$
$$+ z_1 + z_2.$$

The liquidity constraint for period i covers the cumulative cash inflow and outflow from the beginning of the first period to the end of the ith period. Cash collections from sales plus new loans taken less repayments of new loans less any excess cash must equal fixed expenses paid in cash plus minimum ending balance of cash less fixed cash receipts less the beginning balance of cash plus cash payments for new investment plus interest on new loans plus cash payment of variable production costs plus dividends and taxes paid.

The first restriction covers the cash inflow and outflow of the first year. Cash collections from the first year sales are $(0.5)(3x_{11} + 8x_{12})$ and the new loan is y_1. The constant term on the right-hand side includes a number of items. The beginning balance of Accounts Payable is \$ 80, fixed expenses payable in cash in the first year are \$ 30, amortization of long-term debt is \$ 15, payment of dividends \$ 20, and the minimum required ending balance \$ 20. On the other hand, the beginning balance of cash is \$ 50, and the balance of accounts receivable that is collected in the first year is \$ 70. In addition, the first year cash payments include new investment, $60q_1$, and 60 percent of the variable cost of production in the first year, $(0.6)(1.5x_{11} + 5x_{12})$.

The second restriction covers the cash inflows and outflows from the beginning of the first year to the end of the second year. Similarly, the third restriction covers the cash receipts and payments from the beginning of the first year to the end of the third year. The variables v_{13}, v_{23}, and v_{33} indicate any amount of cash in excess of the stipulated minimum balance of \$ 20 at the end of the respective years.

We require that \$ 60 are reserved for investment in the third year. If such a requirement were not made, the model would not invest anything in the last year because this investment would produce growth only in periods which are beyond the cutoff point of the model. This requirement reflects the fact that the cutoff point of any model is always somewhat arbitrary.

Upper Limits of Dividends

$$u_1 + u_{14} = z_1 + (40 - 20),$$
$$(6) \quad u_1 + u_2 + v_{24} = z_1 + z_2 + (40 - 20),$$
$$u_1 + u_2 + u_3 + v_{24} = z_1 + z_2 + z_3 + (40 - 20).$$

Constraints (6) require that the cumulative dividends from the beginning of the first year to the end of the ith year plus any undistributed profit at the end of the ith year must equal the net after tax profit from the beginning of the first year to the end of the ith year.

Dividend Goals

$$
\begin{aligned}
u_1 + v_{15}^- &= 20, \\
(7) \quad u_2 + v_{25}^- &= 22, \\
u_3 + v_{35}^- &= 24.
\end{aligned}
$$

The first year dividend, u_1, plus any negative deviation from the dividend goal, v_{15}^-, must equal the dividend goal for the year, \$20. Similarly, dividends for the remaining years plus any negative deviations are set equal to the respective dividend goals.

The Goals of Earnings Growth

$$
\begin{aligned}
z_1 + v_{16}^- &= (1.2)40 = 48, \\
(8) \quad z_2 + v_{26}^- &= (1.2)z_1, \\
z_3 + v_{36}^- &= (1.2)z_2.
\end{aligned}
$$

The net operating earnings for the year immediatelly preceding the plan (for period $i = 0$) were \$40. Management seeks a growth of 20 percent in annual earnings. The net after tax earnings for the first year, z_1, plus any negative deviation from the goal, v_{16}^-, are therefore set equal to the goal, \$48. The second year earnings, z_2, plus any deviation, v_{26}^-, are similarly set equal to 120 percent of the first year earnings, $(1.2)z_1$. A corresponding interpretation is given to the third year constraint.

Sales Growth

$$
\begin{aligned}
3x_{11} + 8x_{12} + v_{17}^- &= 320, \\
(9) \quad 3x_{21} + 8x_{22} + v_{27}^- &= (1.2)320 = 384, \\
3x_{31} + 8x_{32} + v_{37}^- &= (1.2)384 = 460.
\end{aligned}
$$

The sales goal of the first year is \$320. The left-hand side of the first equation states that the sales for the first year, $3x_{11} + 8x_{12}$, plus any negative deviation from the sales goal, v_{17}^-, must equal the goal. The equations for the following years are given a corresponding interpretation. No overachievement of this goal is sought. Goals are originally set at such high levels that overachievement is not considered to be a possibility.

Nonnegativity Constraints

(10) q_i, x_{1i}, x_{2i}, y_i, z_i, u_i, $v_{ik} \geq 0$, (i = 1, 2, 3),

$\qquad\qquad\qquad\qquad\qquad\qquad\qquad$ (k = 1, 2, ..., 8).

As in any normal linear programming problem we require that all variables must be nonnegative.

The Objective Function

We seek to minimize the negative deviations from the various goals in a given order of preemptive priorities. About the use of the technique see Ijiri.[1] The most important goal is to meet the dividend payments. Therefore, the highest preemptive priority factor, M_4, is associated with the variables v_{i5}^-. The growth of earnings is the second goal in the order of importance. This is indicated by the fact that the second highest preemptive priority factor, M_3, is associated with the variables v_{i6}^-.

In this priority group we wish to make a finer distinction between the various goals. This comes from the fact that the management thinks it is more important to achieve the growth target in the near future than in later years. Therefore, the variables in this priority group are weighted with a discount factor. The first year deviation, v_{16}^-, is multiplied by +1, the second year deviation, v_{26}^-, by $1/(1 + 0.2)$, and the third year deviation, v_{26}^-, by $1/(1+0.2)^2$. The time value of earnings is, in other words, 20 percent.

The next goal on the list of priorities is the sales growth. The priority factor M_2 is associated with the variables v_{i7}^-. No secondary weighting is desired in this priority group and all variables are therefore multiplied by +1.

Finally, we seek to avoid any excessive distortion of the capital structure. Debt may exceed 1.5 time's equity in the first two years, but any such deviations are to be minimized with the lowest order of priorities. It follows that the preemptive priority factor M_1 is associated with the variables v_{12}^+ and v_{22}^+.

---

1 Ijiri, Yuji, Management Goals and Accounting for Control (Amsterdam: North Holland, 1965).

The objective function to be minimized is then

$$Z = M_4 v^-_{15} + M_4 v^-_{25} + M_4 v^-_{35} + M_3 v^-_{16} + \left[1/(1 + 0.2) \right] M_3 v^-_{26} +$$
$$+ \left[1/(1 + 0.2)^2 \right] M_3 v^-_{36} + M_2 v^-_{17} + M_2 v^-_{27} + M_2 v^-_{37} + M_1 v^+_{12} +$$
$$+ M_1 v^+_{22}$$

Solution

The problem was solved utilizing a computer code developed by the author. The code is a modified Simplex procedure which takes into account the fact that in goal programming the objective function and the Simplex criterion are no longer vectors. They are instead matrices which have as many rows as there are levels of priority factors in the problem. In the present model we have four levels of priorities. This means that there are four rows in the respective matrices. It also follows that the shadow prices of goal programming are no longer scalars but vectors with as many elements as there are levels of priority factors.

The solution of the problem is listed in Table 7-1. It can be seen by looking either at the deviations v^-_{15} or at the dividends u_i that the most important goal of the continuation of the dividend policy was exactly met. The deviations are zero and the structural variables are at the level of the goals.

The goal of the net after tax earnings for the first year is \$ 48. The respective variable z_1 has the value of \$ 32.7. This indicates that the goal of earnings growth was not met in the first year. The same can be confirmed by looking at the respective deviation, v^-_{16}, which has the value of \$ 15.3. It can be checked that

$$z_1 + v^-_{16} = 32.7 + 15.3 = 48.$$

The goal of earnings growth is not met in any of the periods, i.e., the other two deviations are also nonzero:

$$v^-_{26} = 3.7, \text{ and } v^-_{36} = 0.9.$$

The firm will also fall short of the goal of sales growth. This is indicated by the fact that the variables showing the negative deviations from the sales goals are all at positive levels:

$$v^-_{17} = 20, \; v^-_{27} = 24, \text{ and } v^-_{37} = 44.$$

It can finally be seen that the goals on capital structure are exactly met in every period:

$$v^+_{12} = 0, \text{ and } v^+_{22} = 0.$$

Structural Variables	Period		
	1	2 ·	3
Sales	x_{11} = 100	x_{21} = 120	x_{31} = 140
	x_{12} = 0	x_{22} = 0	x_{32} = 0
New Loans	y_1 = 45	y_2 = 68	y_3 = 73.6
Investment	q_1 = 1	q_2 = 2	
Net After Tax Profit	z_1 = 32.7	z_2 = 36.6	z_3 = 44
Dividends	u_1 = 20	u_2 = 22	u_3 = 24
Excess Cash	v_{13} = 0	v_{23} = 0	v_{33} = 0
Deviations			
Dividend Goals	v^-_{15} = 0	v^-_{25} = 0	v^-_{35} = 0
Earnings Growth	v^-_{16} = 15.3	v^-_{26} = 3.7	v^-_{36} = 0.9
Sales Growth	v^-_{17} = 20	v^-_{27} = 24	v^-_{37} = 44
Capital Structure	v^+_{12} = 0	v^+_{22} = 0	
	v^-_{12} = 114	v^-_{22} = 113.7	v^-_{32} = 139.4

Table 7-1. Optimal Values of the Variables.

The fact that the negative deviations from the goal of capital structure are all at positive levels indicates that the firm could use even more leverage to obtain faster gorwth if other factors made it advisable and if the direct cost of debt were not excessive in relation to growth possibilities.

It is typical of goal programming problems that some goals are exactly met while others are not. It is also possible that goals of lower priority are exactly met while there are deviations from more important goals. This is exemplified by the goal on capital structure which is met although higher order goals of sales growth and earnings growth are not completely achieved.

It appears advisable to construct the maximum amount of new production capacity in each period:

$$q_1 = 1, \text{ and } q_2 = 1.$$

In this example, the management might want to conduct a sensitivity

	Period No. 1	Period No. 2	Period No. 3
Contribution Margin			
Product A	$1.5x_{11} = (1.5)100 = 150$	$1.5x_{21} = (1.5)120 = 180$	$1.5x_{31} = (1.5)140 = 210$
Product B	$3x_{12} = (3)0 = 0$	$3x_{22} = (3)0 = 0$	$3x_{32} = (3)0 = 0$
Total Contribution	150	180	210
Interest on New Loans	$0.1y_1 = (0.1)45 = 4.5$	$0.1y_2 = (0.1)68 = 6.8$	$0.1y_3 = (0.1)73.6 = 7.4$
	$\overline{145.5}$	$\overline{173.2}$	$\overline{202.6}$
Fixed Expenses	80	82	84
	$\overline{65.5}$	$\overline{91.2}$	$\overline{118.6}$
Depreciation of New Fixed Assets	–	$18q_1 = (18)1 = 18$	$12.6q_1 + 18q_2 = 30.6$
Profit Before Tax	$2z_1 = (2)32.7 = 65.5$	$2z_2 = (2)36.6 = 73.2$	$2z_3 = (2)44 = 88$
Income Tax	$z_1 = 32.7$	$z_2 = 36.6$	$z_3 = 44$
Net Operating Earnings	$z_1 = \overline{32.7}$	$z_2 = \overline{36.6}$	$z_3 = \overline{44}$

Table 7-2. Projected Income Statements.

	Period No. 1	Period No. 2	Period No. 3
Assets			
Cash	20	20	20
Accaounts Receivable	$1.5x_{11}$ = 150	$1.5x_{21}$ = 180	$1.5x_{31}$ = 210
Inventories	150	150	150
Fixed Assets	300	330	345
Depreciation	30 270	45 285	55.6 289.4
New Acquisition	60 330	60 345	60 349.4
Total	650	695	729.4
Liabilities			
Accounts Payable	60	72	84
Variable Costs $(0.4)1.5x_{1l}$	20	22	24
Accrued Fixed Expenses	32.7	36.6	44
Income Tax z_i	4.5 117.2	6.8 137.4	7.4 159.4
Accrued Interest $0.1y_i$	45	68.3	73.6
New Loans y_i	200	185	170
Long-Term Loans	15 185	15 170	15 155
Amortization			
Equity	290	302.7	319.3
Dividends u_i	20 270	20 282.7	22 297.3
Net Operating Earnings z_i	32.7 302.7	36.6 319.3	44 341.3
Total	650	695	729.3

Table 7-3. Projected Balance Sheets.

analysis after the first solution and explore the possibility of constructing more new production capacity by using additional borrowed capital if this

	Period No.		
	1	2	3
Sources of Funds			
Net Earnings	32.7	36.6	44
Depreciation	30	45	55.6
	62.7	81.6	99.6
Uses of Funds			
Investment	60	60	60
Dividends	20	20	22
Amortization of			
Long-Term Loans	15	15	15
	95	95	97
Net Change in			
Working Capital	(32.3)	(13.4)	(2.6)
	62.7	81.6	99.6

Table 7-4. Projected Changes in Working Capital.

were technically feasible. Even if additional capacity were to cost more than $ 60 per unit assumed in the example, its construction might bring the firm closer to the goals of earnings and sales. However, it is clear from the solution that earnings growth goal cannot be met in the first year because new investment will increase sales and profits from the second year on.

It is also possible to generate conventional financial forecasts on the basis of the solution. This has been done in Tables 7-2 to 7-4 which give the projected income statement, the projected balance sheet, and the projected sources and uses of funds for each year of the model. There may be advantages in presenting the solution in this form. It may be easier to communicate with managers with the help of these projections because managers are more used to financial forecasts than to computer output that lists a number of variables and their optimal values. The values of the variables indicate the physical sales, production, invest-ment, and other programs that are consistent with these budgets. In other words, it is possible to combine the planning of both physical facilities and finances with the help of the model. It is also clear from the formulation of the model and its solution that the distinction between operating and capital budgets tends to disappear when firms begin to use strategic planning models.

Conclusion

The presentation of the goal programming model of this chapter was not made implying that all strategic planning will be encompassed by formal optimization models. Significant areas of strategic planning may never be formalized to the extent required by optimization models. The analysis of the firm´s environment and the search for new opportunities will require intuition and be more art than science for many years to come.

There are already at this stage distinct advantages to be achieved by building of strategic models, however. One of these advantages may be the fact that in order to build models of manageable size we must heavily aggregate the variables that we would like to use, say, in one year budget models. This forces one to concentrate on the really important things.

Another advantage is that in order to work with formal optimization models we must think hard about the goals to be optimized. Since it is unlikely that we could reduce these goals into a single overall measure, we must learn to analyze sets of goals. Goal programming can be of great help in this analysis.

APPENDIX

Solution to the sample problem of chapter 1, equations (1-1) through (1-5) with IBM 1130 computer code MOSS

==

In order to prepare the input cards e must give names to the columns and the rows of the problem.

The following names are used for the sample problem:

	X1	X2	RESTRIC
CONTRIB	600.	200.	
SALEA	1.		6.
SALEB		1.	10.
CAPACITY	10.	20.	160.
CASH	300.	200.	2400.

The required input cards can now be prepared as follows:

JOB **SAMPLE PROBLEM** ANALYST _____ DATE // PAGE **1** OF **2**

	INDICATOR Type 2-3	NAME 1 5-12	NAME 2 15-22	VALUE 2 25-30-36	NAME 3 40-47	VALUE 50-55-62
1	//	JOB				
2	//	XEQ MOSS				
3	INPUT					
4	NAME		SAMPLE			
5		X1	CONTRIB	600.		
6		X1	SALEA	1.		
7		X1	CAPACITY	10.		
8		X1	CASH	300.		
9		X2	CONTRIB	200.		
10		X2	SALEB	1.		
11		X2	CAPACITY	20.		
12		X2	CASH	200.		
13	FR	RESTRIC	CONTRIB			
14	UB	RESTRIC	SALEA	6.		
15	UB	RESTRIC	SALEB	10.		
16	UB	RESTRIC	CAPACITY	160.		
17	UB	RESTRIC	CASH	2400.		
18	ENDATA					
19						
20						

Appendix

JOB **SAMPLE PROBLEM** ANALYST _____ DATE // PAGE **2** OF **2**

	INDICATOR Type 2-3	NAME 1 5-12	NAME 2 15-22	VALUE 2 25-30-36	NAME 3 40-47	VALUE 50-55-62
1	MOVE					
2		DATA	SAMPLE			
3		MAXIMIZE	CONTRIB			
4		BOUNDS	RESTRIC			
5	ENDATA					
6	LPSOLUTION					
7	DELETE					
8		DATA	SAMPLE			
9	ENDATA					
10	END					
11						
12						
13						
14						
15						
16						
17						
18						
19						
20						

Appendix

Solution to the Sample Problem in the Appendix.

VARIABLE	TYPE	ENTRIES	SOLUTION ACTIVITY	UPPER BOUND	LOWER BOUND	CURRENT COST	REDUCED COST
X1	B*	4	6.000	**********	0.000	600.000	0.000
CONTRIB	B*	0	4200.000	**********	**********	-1.000	-1.000
SALEA	UL	0	6.000	6.000	0.000	0.000	-300.000
CAPACITYB*		0	120.000	160.000	0.000	0.000	0.000
CASH	UL	0	2400.000	2400.000	0.000	0.000	-1.000
X2	B*	4	3.000	**********	0.000	200.000	0.000
SALEB	B*	0	3.000	10.000	0.000	0.000	0.000

Bibliography

General Readings

Charnes, A., and Cooper, W.W., Management Models and Industrial Applications of Linear Programming, Vol. 1 & 2 (New York: Wiley, 1961)

Charnes, A., Cooper, W.W., and Miller, M.H., "Application of Linear Programming to Financial Budgeting and the Costing of Funds", Journal of Business, Vol. XXXII, No. 1 (January, 1959), pp. 20-46

Ijiri, Yuji, Management Goals and Accounting for Control (Amsterdam: North Holland, 1965)

Jääskeläinen, Veikko, Optimal Financing and Tax Policy of the Corporation (Helsinki: The Helsinki Research Institute for Business Economics, 1966)

Lee, Sang, Goal Programming for Decision Analysis (Philadelphia, N.J.: Auerbach, 1972)

Mao, James C.T., Quantitative Analysis of Financial Decisions (New York: Macmillan, 1969)

Weingartner, H. Martin, Mathematical Programming and the Analysis of Capital Budgeting Problems (Englewood Cliffs, N.J.: Prentice-Hall, 1963)

Strategic Planning Models

Carleton, Willard T., "An Analytical Model for Long Range Financial Planning", The Journal of Finance (1970), pp. 291-315

Dickens, Jared H., "Linear Programming in Corporate Simulation", in Albert N. Schrieber (ed.), Corporate Simulation Models (Seattle, Wash.: University of Washington, 1970), pp. 292-314

Hamilton, William F., and Moses, Michael A., "An Optimization Model for Corporate Financial Planning", Operations Research, Vol. 21, No. 3 (May-June, 1973), pp. 677-692

Hayes, Robert H., and Nolan, Richard L., "What Kind of Corporate Modeling Functions Best", Harvard Business Review (May-June, 1974), pp. 102-112

Jääskeläinen, Veikko, "A Goal Programming Model of Bank Long-Range Financial Planning, " The Finnish Journal of Business Economics, No. 4 (1972), pp. 408-421

Jääskeläinen, Veikko, "Strategic Planning with Goal Programming", Management Informatics, Vol. 1, No. 1 (February, 1972), pp. 23-30

Jääskeläinen, Veikko, and Lee, Sang, "A Goal Programming Model for Financial Planning", The Finnish Journal of Business Economics, No. 3 (1971), pp. 291-303

Myers, Steward C., and Pogue, Gerald A., "A Programming Approach to Corporate Financial Management", Journal of Finance (May, 1974), pp. 579-599

Tietotehdas, Yritysmalli - käyttäjän käsikirja (Corporate Model: The User's Manual - manual to a generalized computer model which simultaneously generates the sales, production, profit, financing, and capital budgets for industrial firms based on a linear programming model) (Helsinki, 1974)

Budget Models

Chervany, Norman L., Strom, John S., and Boehlke, Ralph F., "An Operations Planning Model for the Northwestern National Bank of Minneapolis, " in Albert N. Schrieber (ed.), Corporate Simulation Models (Seattle, Wash.: University of Washington, 1970), pp. 208-245

Cohen, Kalman J., and Thore, Sten, "Programming Bank Portfolios under Uncertainty", Journal of Bank Research (Spring, 1970)

Driebeek, Norman J., Applied Linear Programming (Reading, Mass.: Addison-Wesley, 1969)

Jääskeläinen, Veikko, and Salmi, Timo, "Joint Determination of Production and Financial Budgets of a Multinational Firm Facing Risky Currency Exchange Rates", paper presented at the Meeting on Financial Theory and Decision Models in Garmisch-Partenkirchen, West-Germany (June, 1974)

Mehta, Dileep R., and Inselbag, Isik, "Working Capital Management of a Multinational Firm", in S. Prakash Sethi, and Jagdish N. Sheth (editors), Multinational Business Operations IV: Financial Management (Pacific Palisades, Ca: Goodyear, 1973)

Petty II, John William, An Optimal Transfer-Pricing System for The Multinational Firm: A Linear Programming Approach (Austin, Texas: The University of Texas at Austin, 1971), Doctoral Dissertation

Salmi, Timo, The Multinational Firm, A Mathematical Programming Model Building Approach (Helsinki: The Helsinki School of Economics, 1973)

Cash Management Models

Lietaer, Bernard A., Financial Management of Foreign Exchange: An Operational Technique to Reduce Risk (Cambridge, Mass.: The M.I.T. Press, 1971)

Näykki, Pertti, Kassavarannon optimointimalli (A Combined Markovian and Linear Programming Model for Optimizing Cash Reserves (Turku, Finland: The University of Turku, 1971) unpublished thesis

Orgler, Yair, Cash Management Methods and Models (Belmont, Ca: Wadsworth, 1970)

Pogue, Gerald A., and Bussard, Ralph N., "A Linear Programming Model for Short Term Financial Planning under Uncertainty", Sloan Management Review (Spring, 1972), pp. 69-97

Robichek, A.A., Teichroew, D., and Jones, J.M., "Optimal Short Term Financing Decision", Management Science, Vol. 12 (September, 1965), pp. 1-36

Shapiro, Alan Charles, Management Science Models for Multicurrency Cash Management (Pittsburgh, Pa: Carnegie-Mellon University, 1971), Doctoral Dissertation

Srinivasan, V., "A Transshipment Model for Cash Management Decisions," Management Science (June, 1974), pp. 1350-1363

Budget Control

Demski, Joel S., "An Accounting System Structured on a Linear Programming Model", The Accounting Review (October, 1967), pp. 701-712

Jääskeläinen, Veikko, "Traditional and Ex-Post Variance Analysis: A Reconciliation", The Finnish Journal of Business Economics, No. 2 (1969), pp. 1-18